THE HELEN REGENSTEIN COLLECTION OF EUROPEAN DRAWINGS

The Helen Regenstein Collection of European Drawings

CATALOGUE BY HAROLD JOACHIM

THE ART INSTITUTE OF CHICAGO • 1974

The Art Institute of Chicago

Copyright © 1974 The Art Institute of Chicago
Library of Congress Catalog Card Number: 74-79440
Design by Everett McNear
Composition and printing
by Hillison & Etten Company

Preface

The Art Institute of Chicago has been extremely fortunate in its nearly 100 years of existence to have had a group of distinguished collectors, who eventually became our benefactors and laid the cornerstone for our great collections. To mention just a few—in a class by themselves were the Martin Ryersons, who collected works of art from the 14th Century until the 20th Century. To these, important Impressionists were added from the Potter Palmers; Mrs. L. L. Coburn; and the Helen Birch Bartlett Collection, which includes the renowned Seurat. Later came the Joseph Winterbotham Collection. Gifts from the Chauncey McCormicks and the Charles Worcesters increased our holdings of earlier paintings. Kate S. Buckingham and Russell Tyson initiated our distinguished holdings in Oriental art. Robert Allerton stands alone for his great contributions in almost every field and his outstanding bequest. In the field of drawings, Mrs. Tiffany Blake showed rare judgment in her selection. Each of these had in common the greatest of taste and humility of giving.

To this eminent roster, it is the Trustees' and my pleasure to add the name of Mrs. Joseph Regenstein. Her artistic interests are concentrated in two areas: Oriental, particularly Japanese, painting and sculpture, and European drawings before 1900. The eighty-two drawings she has given us in recent years are of the highest quality and make the Art Institute Drawing Collection the envy of all other museums in the country specializing in this area. Seeing them all together in our new Print and Drawing Galleries, which she so generously helped rehabilitate, will be a joy forever—not only to Chicagoans, but to visitors from all over the world.

We are indeed greatly indebted to Helen Regenstein and the Joseph and Helen Regenstein Foundation.

LEIGH B. BLOCK
Chairman of the Board

Mrs. Regenstein, one of the Art Institute's great benefactors, belongs to that truly elect and small group which is satisfied only with the best. And it is the best she has demanded and made possible for us to acquire. Thus, she has added not only to the pleasure of the discriminating public but to the joy of the professional staff.

JOHN MAXON
*Vice-President for
Collections and Exhibitions*

Introduction

Helen Regenstein began acquiring drawings for The Art Institute in 1958 through the Joseph and Helen Regenstein Foundation. The first drawing was the splendid Watteau, *Three Studies of a Woman,* which at once established the high standard of quality as well as the gracious keynote for the entire collection. In the fifteen years since that time, she has assembled a group of drawings, pastels and watercolors which in harmonious consistency is surely unique among collections formed in that period anywhere. It was her choice to concentrate on French masters of the eighteenth and nineteenth centuries as well as on Italian masters of the eighteenth century. Although there are five earlier works and one Goya drawing, this concentration has resulted in an ensemble more satisfying than a wider inclusion of other countries and centuries could have achieved. Many of the works are well-known in the literature, but numerous others are published here for the first time, such as five drawings by Lancret, two by Magnasco and eight of the nine Piazzetta drawings which only recently came from the descendants of the distinguished patron for whom they were made.

Although I have had the great privilege of serving as an advisor to Helen Regenstein, the final decision has always been hers. Thus her collection, which will be shown this spring for the first time in the newly created Helen Regenstein Gallery, stands as a lasting monument to her taste, sense of beauty, and enlightened humanism which characterize everything she has done for The Art Institute as well as for the whole community.

It is my pleasure to thank the staff of the Department of Prints and Drawings, Anselmo Carini and Esther Sparks, as well as former and temporary staff members, Gretchen Anderson, Rafael Fernandez, Betsy Fryberger, and Devin Burnell, for their help in assembling the catalogue notes. I also wish to express my appreciation to Howard Kraywinkel and John Mahtesian for their excellent photographs of the works reproduced here.

HAROLD JOACHIM
Curator of Prints and Drawings

Index

On the cover:

Watteau, *The Old Savoyard,* no. 26

On the endleaves: Detail from
Fragonard, *Arbor with Two Children,* no. 48

Vittore Carpaccio   Venice, ca. 1460/65 - 1523/26

1   *Two Kneeling Clerics* (recto)
Standing Youth (verso)
Grey and black wash heightened with white over
black chalk on blue-grey paper
195 x 253 mm   1962.577
Collections:
Lt. Col. Norman R. Colville

Dr. Francis Springell   Sale: London, Sotheby,
June 28, 1962, no. 13 reproduced

Acquired from Richard H. Zinser, New York
Publications:
H. Tietze and E. Tietze-Conrat, *The Drawings of
the Venetian Painters of the 15th and 16th
Centuries,* New York, 1944, p. 153, no. 618, pl.
XVI 3 (recto) and XXII 2 (verso)

G. Fiocco, *Carpaccio,* Novara, 1958, p. 29, no. 3

J. Lauts, *Carpaccio: Paintings and Drawings,*
London, 1962, p. 272, no. 31, fig. 120 (verso) and
fig. 139 (recto)

J. Maxon, A Sheet of Drawings by Carpaccio,
The Art Institute of Chicago Quarterly, LVI no.
4, Winter 1962/63, pp. 62-64, reproduced p. 62
(verso) and p. 64 (recto)

G. Perocco, *Carpaccio nella Scuola di S. Giorgio
degli Schiavoni,* Venice, 1964, p. 79, fig. 53 (verso)
reproduced

M. Muraro, *Carpaccio,* Florence, 1966, p. 109
Exhibitions:
1963 Venice, Palazzo Ducale, *Vittore Carpaccio,*
p. 298 no. 24 reproduced
1963 Wildenstein, New York, *Master Drawings
from The Art Institute of Chicago* (hereafter cited
as "1963 Wildenstein"), no. 4 reproduced

Drawings done with a finely pointed brush in black
and white on blue paper are a Venetian speciality,
developed in the fifteenth century. Such drawings
would not be the first concepts for paintings, but
rather preliminary studies for individual figures
whose roles in the paintings had already been de-
termined. The elegant *Standing Youth* appears with
slight variations in the center of *St. Tryphon and
the Basilisk* in the Scuola di San Giorgio degli
Schiavoni (1507-1508), and the *Two Kneeling
Clerics* was destined for *The Pope Presenting a
Ceremonial Parasol to Doge Sebastiano Ziano,* from
the History of Ancona cycle in the Sala del Gran
Consiglio of the Doge's Palace in Venice. The
painting was destroyed by fire in 1577, but the
E.B. Crocker Art Gallery in Sacramento, California,
owns a preliminary pen drawing (Tietze, no. 635)
for the center part of the composition, which shows
the two kneeling figures in a few precise strokes of
the pen.

9

Alessandro Magnasco   Genoa 1667 - 1749

2   *Ballad Singer with a Shrine to the Virgin*
Brown wash heightened with white over black
chalk on buff paper
466 x 370 mm   1962.585

Collections:

Gentile de Giuseppe, Paris

Dr. Wertheimer, Paris

Acquired from Slatkin, New York

Publications:

J. Scholz, "Drawings by Alessandro Magnasco,"
*Essays in the History of Art Presented to R.
Wittkower,* London, 1967, p. 239. (refers
briefly to both sheets 1962.585 and 586)

Galerie Charpentier, Paris, Sale May 24, 1955,
no. 131 reproduced

Exhibitions:

1963 Wildenstein, no. 12

Magnasco's fantastic and bizarre romanticism was
much appreciated in his own time, detested in the
nineteenth century, and again admired in our
century. His life began and ended in Genoa, but
his most creative years were spent in Milan, where
he was deeply impressed by the prevailing Spanish-
Jesuit atmosphere. He also spent a few years in
Florence, where he may have discovered his affinity
to the spirit of Jacques Callot. His own life is
reported to have been as bohemian as his art suggests, and many of his works dealing with vaga-
bonds, gypsies, soldiers, and artists' studios in
cavernous cellars, may have an autobiographical
undertone.

There are few among his many drawings
which can compare with the pair of magnificent
sheets in the Regenstein Collection. The nervous,
flickering vibrancy of his brush technique (there
is no pen work, only underlying sketches in black
chalk) ideally fits the subjects. Similar themes occur
in his paintings, but the compositions are never
identical. The traveling shrine of the Madonna in
a grotto occurs again in a painting in the Gatti-
Casazza Collection, Venice (*Mostra del Magnasco,*
Genoa, 1949, no. 7). The picaresque group in an
artist's studio, with Magnasco's favorite parapher-
nalia, a monkey and a magpie, is linked with many
scenes of groups in ruined, cluttered cellars (cf.
Woman and Soldiers at Table, M.H. De Young
Museum, San Francisco, as well as no. 54 in the
above cited catalogue).

Alessandro Magnasco

3   *Picaresque Group with a Monkey and a Magpie*
     Brown wash heightened with white over black
     chalk on buff paper
     477 x 370 mm   1962.586
     Collections:
     Gentile de Giuseppe, Paris

     Dr. Wertheimer, Paris

     Acquired from Slatkin, New York

     Publications:
     (as before)

     Exhibitions:
     1963 Wildenstein, no. 13

4   *Portrait of Field Marshal*
Count von der Schulenburg
Black and white chalk on ivory paper
501 x 379 mm   1971.325

Collections:
Count Johann Matthias von der Schulenburg
and Descendants
Acquired from Paul Drey Gallery, New York
(9 drawings 1971.325-333)

Publications:
A. Morassi, "Settecento Inedito," *Arte Veneta*, VI,
1952, pp. 85-91, reproduced
R. Pallucchini, *Piazzetta,* Milan, 1956 reproduced
A. Binion, "From Schulenburg's Gallery and
Records," *The Burlington Magazine,* CXII, no.
806, May 1970, p. 301
Gazette des Beaux-Arts, LXXXI, no. 1249, Fevrier
1973, p. 129, no. 458 reproduced

It is to one of the most extraordinary charac-
ters of eighteenth-century Venice that we owe this
spectacular group of Piazzetta heads, Field Marshal
Johann Matthias von Schulenburg, whose impres-
sive portrait is here included. Born in 1661, in
Emden near Magdeburg, his military career was
spent in the service of the Hapsburgs. Upon his
retirement, the Venetian Republic asked Schulenburg to take charge of their defenses against the
Turks. He came to Venice in 1715, and his successful conquest of the enemy at Corfu saved the Republic from further danger. He served Venice for
thirty years, died in Verona in 1747, and is en-
tombed in the Arsenal in Venice.

The Field Marshal began collecting pictures
in 1724. He hired artists, among them Antonio
Guardi and Pittoni, as well as Piazzetta later, to

act as copyists, agents, restorers and appraisers. His
account books were carefully kept, and show that
his relationship with Piazzetta began in 1731, with
a payment for two drawings of heads *(teste)*. The
last note is for 5 December 1745. He collected more
Piazzettas than any other patron of his time: thir-
teen paintings and at least nineteen drawings. Fifteen of these were heads and portraits, done in the
early 1730's.

Schulenburg willed his collection to his
nephew with instructions that it be kept together
in Berlin; his wishes were not respected and sales
were made a few years after his death. For example,
the two oil paintings by Piazzetta, *Beggar Boy* and
Pastorale, in the Art Institute collection were sold
from the Schulenburg collection in London in 1775.
The nine drawings that are described here came
from the part of the collection remaining in the
family castle, Hehlen an der Weser, until recent
years.

Piazzetta, born in Venice but largely trained
in Bologna (1703-1711), must certainly be considered, next to G. Battista Tiepolo, the greatest
Venetian painter in the first half of the eighteenth
century. Yet he was not a prolific painter, and his
great fame in his time (and still today) rested to a
large degree on his extraordinarily vivacious and
full-bodied character studies of the Venetian popu-
lace, drawn in black and white chalks on buff
paper. In this genre, Piazzetta had several imitators,
of which Maggiotto was the best, and there are
cases where the authorship is doubtful, especially
if the condition of the drawings has suffered by
rubbing and retracing. Therefore, the recent emer-
gence from relative obscurity of an untouched
group of drawings with an impeccable history may
be considered a joyous event for all friends of
Venetian art.

19

Giovanni Battista Piazzetta

7   *Boy Feeding a Dog*
(ca. 1730)
Black and white chalk
527 x 410 mm   1971.326

Collections:
(as before)

It is easy to understand why this drawing was particularly valued by Piazzetta, who sold it for six zecchini in October 1739 and appraised it at twenty a few years later. The Art Institute painting of *The Beggar Boy* (Worcester Collection, 1930. 747) uses the same model in an identical costume. Our drawing is also closely related to the two sheets from the Walter C. Baker Collection (J. Bean and F. Stampfle, *Drawings from New York Collections III, The Eighteenth Century in Italy,* New York 1971, nos. 40 and 41). In *Young People Feeding a Dog* (no. 40) the boy is offering to the dog the same kind of twisted roll *(cornuto)* as in the Regenstein drawing.

8   Giovanni Battista Piazzetta

Portrait of a Young Boy (ca. 1730)
Black and white chalk 384 x 291 mm   1971.330
Collections: (as before)

9   Giovanni Battista Piazzetta

Portrait of a Man (ca. 1730)

Black and white chalk 388 x 287 mm   1971.333

Collections: (as before)

10   Giovanni Battista Piazzetta

Portrait of a Young Woman (ca. 1730)
Black and white chalk 388 x 290 mm   1971.332
Collections: (as before)

11 Giovanni Battista Piazzetta

Portrait of a Gondolier (ca. 1730)
Black and white chalk 388 x 291 mm 1971.331
Collections: (as before)

Giovanni Battista Piazzetta

12   *Portrait of a Young Man Holding a Sword*
      (ca. 1730)
      Black and white chalk
      388 x 287 mm   1971.329
      Collections:
      (as before)

13 *The Temptation of Saint Anthony* ca. 1730-34
Graphite, pen and wash in brown ink, heightened
with white, over black chalk on white paper
Watermark: Three crescents (similar to Heawood
865)
402 x 250 mm   1964.347

Collections:
Pietro Monaco
Davide Antonio Fosati (Galerie Pardo)
Leo Franklyn
Acquired from Slatkin, New York

Publications:
G. Knox, "A Group of Tiepolo Drawings Owned
and Engraved by Pietro Monaco," *Master
Drawings,* III, no. 4, 1965, pp. 389-397, reproduced
on cover

Exhibitions:
1970 Cambridge, Mass., Fogg Art Museum,
Harvard University, *Tiepolo: A Bicentenary
Exhibition,* no 11 reproduced

This drawing is so highly finished that it must have
been intended as a presentation piece or as a model
for an engraving. It is one of eight drawings by
Giambattista which were owned and engraved by
Pietro Monaco (1707-1772), who established himself as a portrait engraver in Venice about 1732.
The reverse of our drawing bears the following
inscription in ink: "vdi 4 Marzo 1760 Venezia dal
Sig.ᴿ Davide Ant. Fosati o riceputo io Pietro Monaco cecchini tre e questo per pagamento del Pre-
sente disegno originale de Sig.ᴿ Gio Batta Tiepolo
al 260." (Both the inscription and the Monaco
engraving are reproduced in *Master Drawings,* vol.
3, no. 4, 1965, pp. 389 ff.) The drawing is rich in
subtle gradations of wash, ranging from the light-
est grey-brown to a deep black-brown. The crowded
composition has an almost Northern Gothic flavor.
The interplay of expressive hands and the face of
the snub-nosed urchin devil are vaguely reminiscent of Schongauer and Dürer prints, which were
probably known to Tiepolo. Knox dates this drawing 1730-34.

Giovanni Battista Tiepolo

14   *Fantasy on the Death of Seneca*
(ca. 1740)
Pen and wash in brown ink over black chalk
on white paper
340 x 240 mm   1959.36
Collections:
Gustave Deloye, Paris (Lugt 756).
Sale: Paris, June 12-15, 1899, no. 132
Ferdinand Roybet, Paris.
Sale: Paris, Hotel Drouot, Dec. 14-16, 1920, no. 25
Lucien Guiraud, Paris.
Sale: Paris, Hotel Drouot, June 14-16, 1956,
no. 68 reproduced
Acquired from Knoedler & Co., New York
Publications:
Art Quarterly, XXII, no. 4 Winter 1959,
p. 396 reproduced
H. Joachim, "A Late Tiepolo Drawing," *The
Art Institute of Chicago Quarterly,* LIII, no. 4,
February 1960, pp. 18-19 reproduced
Exhibitions:
1952 Paris, Galerie Cailleux, *Tiepolo et Guardi,*
no. 22 reproduced
1958 M. Knoedler & Co., London, *Exhibition of
Old Master, Impressionist and Contemporary
Drawings,* no. 5
1963 Wildenstein, no. 16 reproduced
1970 Cambridge no. 16 reproduced

The drawing is by no means a plausible illustration of the tragic end of the Roman philosopher, who was bidden by Nero to commit suicide. It is rather a free fantasy on that theme, spiced with whimsical elements of a masquerade. In spirit and composition it comes close to the etchings, *Scherzi di fantasia,* of the 1740's, and the drawing probably belongs to that period. The brilliant luminosity of the wash, the effective distribution of accents and the economy of means show the artist at his full maturity. A little detail should be mentioned which seems to have escaped notice in literature. At times, Tiepolo appears to have enjoyed drawing on slightly creased papers which make pen and brush skip, thereby heightening the desired effect of decay. The flaw in the paper is even more conspicuous in another Art Institute drawing, *Two Monks in Meditation* (no. 1931. 454).

Giovanni Battista Tiepolo

15 *Punchinellos' Repast*
Ink and brown wash over pencil on ivory paper
196 x 228 mm   1972.108

Collections:
Italico Brass, Venice

Acquired from E. V. Thaw, New York

Exhibitions:
1965 Udine, Loggia del Lionello,
Disegni del Tiepolo, no. 48 reproduced

Punchinello, versatile character in the commedia dell'arte, is the subject of some of Giambattista's most humorous and light-hearted drawings. Of Neapolitan origin, Punchinello was first introduced onto the stage by the Neapolitan actor Silvio Fiorillo around 1600. According to legend, Punchinello was known in farces even in Roman times. Giambattista depicted similar scenes of Punchinellos in a painting, *Punchinellos' Kitchen,* (Paris, Cailleux Collection, ca. 1760-70), and in a drawing in Trieste, Museo Civico.

The lightly sketched figure in the center of the Regenstein drawing attests to the spontaneous evolution of Battista's composition. The sparkling effect of the wash is characteristic of drawings from the seventeen-forties. Morassi proposes a date shortly before 1740 for our sheet (Udine, 1965, no. 48). Other excellent examples of Battista's drawings of Punchinellos are preserved in the E.V. Thaw Collection, New York; the Shickman Gallery, New York; and the Fondazione Cini, Venice. Knox dates most of these drawings around 1760.

16 *Rest on the Flight into Egypt*
Pen and brown ink with grey wash on ivory paper
285 x 205 mm   1968.311

Collections:
Edward Cheney (?). Sale: London,
Sotheby & Co., 29 April 1885
Alessandro Contini, Rome

Mrs. D. Kilvert, New York

Acquired from Rosenberg & Stiebel, New York

Publications:
U. Ojetti, *II Settecento Italiano,* I, Milan/Rome,
1932 (reproduced Pl. CXCII, fig. 289)

Tiepolo, the lyrical poet, is nowhere more eloquent than in his inexhaustible variations on the subject of the *Holy Family on the Flight into Egypt*. They were probably done around 1760, prior to the artist's departure for Spain, and they represent the last phase of his drawing style where all nonessential detail is omitted and forms are rather suggested than articulated. As Knox (no. 89, *Tiepolo, . . . ,* Fogg Art Museum, 1970) says, "They float on the page like exquisite arabesques, a marvellous monument to Giambattista's talent and virtuosity as a draughtsman."

Giovanni Domenico Tiepolo   Venice 1727 - 1804

17   *The Wedding of Punchinello*
Pen and brown ink with brown wash over pencil
on ivory paper Inscribed on pillar: *Dom Tiepolo f*
350 x 467 mm   1968.312
Collections:
Duc de Talleyrand
Acquired from Rosenberg & Stiebel, New York

Active for many years as an able assistant to his
father in the execution of frescoes, Domenico
Tiepolo became a major artist in his own right, and
particularly as a draughtsman he developed a dis-
tinctly individual style, marked by a nervous staccato
rather than the sweeping legato lines of the elder
Tiepolo. His inexhaustible, whimsical imagination
reveals itself to best advantage in the sets of scenes
from contemporary life, and most of all, in the 102
drawings of Punchinellos in all sorts of activities
and situations. One of the most charming of these
is the *Wedding of Punchinello,* which is actually a
parody of the splendid ceiling fresco in Würzburg,
The Wedding of Barbarossa. No one knows
whether the elder Tiepolo would have approved
of this kind of spoof, but he was no longer alive,
and the whole splendor of eighteenth-century
Venice was about to vanish when these drawings
were made. They are a last nostalgic farewell to
the eighteenth century.

37

Francesco Zuccarelli   Pitigliano, 1702 - Florence 1788

18   *Portrait of an Old Man*
Black and white chalk on blue-grey paper
201 x 165 mm   1960.560
Acquired from Kleinberger & Co., New York
Exhibitions:
1963 Wildenstein, no. 19

The artist is generally considered a member of the Venetian School, though he was Tuscan by birth and did not go to Venice until he was almost thirty. His idyllic landscapes made him very popular all over Europe, including England, where in 1768 he became one of the founding members of the Royal Academy. A hitherto unknown facet of his art came to light with the fairly recent discovery of an album of drawings made for Count Francesco Maria Tassi in 1748 (R. Bassi-Rathgeb, *Un Album inedito di Francesco Zuccarelli,* Bergamo, 1949), namely his very lively and realistic portraits, done in a rapid and nervous, yet purposeful style. The Chicago drawing and two others in the Duc de Talleyrand Collection (A. Morassi, *Dessins Vénitiens du dix-huitième Siècle de la Collection du Duc de Talleyrand,* Milan, 1958, pls. 77-78) reveal the same hand as the Bergamo album.

19   *Capriccio with a Squall on the Lagoon*
Pen and brown ink with brown wash over
black chalk on ivory paper
270 x 382 mm   1968.309
Collections:
Lucille Cohen, Paris

Bloch, Paris

Marquis de Biron

Duc de Talleyrand

Acquired from Rosenberg & Stiebel, New York
Publications:
A. Morassi, *Dessins Vénitiens du 18ème Siècle de
la Collection du Duc de Talleyrand,* Milan, 1958,
no. 69 reproduced
Exhibitions:
1952 Paris Galerie Cailleux, *Tiepolo et Guardi,*
no. 108

1960/61 Paris, Petit-Palais,
Peinture Italienne au XVIIIe Siècle, no. 310

The stormy execution of this exotic drawing points
to the very last years of Guardi's life. Another drawing with the same composition exists (Collection
E.V. Thaw, *Drawings from New York Collections
III,* no. 205), and both are autograph works.

41

Francesco Guardi

20 *Capriccio with a Gateway near a Landing Bridge*
Pen and brown wash over black chalk
on ivory paper
303 x 451 mm   1968.310
Collections:
(as before)
Publications:
A. Morassi, 1958, no. 67 reproduced
Exhibitions:
1952 Paris, no. 109
1960/61 Paris, no. 311

This is a particularly splendid example of the land-scape *capriccio* from the artist's later years. The rough underdrawing in pencil is clearly visible and has often been ignored by the final, entirely sponta-neous execution with pen and brush. The same composition, with minor variations, can be found in paintings in the Uffizi (V. Moschini, *Francesco Guardi,* Milan, 1952, pl. 175), and in the Metro-politan Museum (P. Zampetti, *I Vedutisti Ven-eziani del Settecento,* Venice, 1967, fig. 154).

Mauro Antonio Tesi (Maurino) Modena 1730 - Bologna 1766

21 *Architectural Fantasy* (recto)
Architectural Detail: Arches, Window, etc. (verso)
Pen and brown ink, brown wash,
touched with watercolor
277 x 187 mm 1959.185

Collections:
Armando Perera, Rome
Edmond Fatio Sale: Geneva, N. Rauch, S.A.,
1959, no. 10 reproduced
Acquired from William H. Schab, New York

Exhibitions:
1961 Minneapolis, University Gallery, University
of Minnesota, *The Eighteenth Century, One
Hundred Drawings by One Hundred Artists,*
no. 5 reproduced
1963 Wildenstein, no. 10
1965 New Orleans, Tulane University,
Drawings and Architecture, no. 4 reproduced
1968 Philadelphia Museum of Art,
Drawings by the Bibiena Family, no. 11

Listed in the Fatio sale catalogue as a work by
Ferdinando Galli de Bibiena, the drawing has more
recently been considered to be by Mauro Tesi
(Janos Scholz and others). The flamboyant and
painterly interpretation of architecture in this
warmly colored drawing is unusual for a member
of the Bibiena family. If the album of architectural
fantasies in the Ashmolean is the work of Tesi
(*Italian Drawings from the Ashmolean Museum,
Oxford, A Loan Exhibition . . ., at Wildenstein &
Co.,* London, 1970, nos. 72-74), the Art Institute
sheet would also have to be assigned to him.

22   *The Dancing Girl (Be Careful with that Step)*
Unfinished sketch of a dancer, verso
Inscribed in pencil: *Cuydado con ese paso/30*
Grey and black wash on ivory paper
Watermark: Honig and Zoonen
263 x 182 mm   1958.542
Collections:
Javier Goya, Madrid

Mariano Goya, Madrid

Valentin Carderera, Madrid (?)

Monsieur X. . . ,   Sale: Paris, Hotel Drouot,
April 3, 1877, no. 95

Paul Meurice, Paris
Sale: Paris, Hotel Drouot, May 25, 1966, no. 92

Monsieur X., Paris, Galerie Charpentier,
April 9, 1957, no. 6 reproduced

Acquired from Rosenberg and Stiebel, New York
Publications:
E. Crispolti, "Disegni inediti di Goya," *Commentari*,
IX, no. 2, April-June 1958, pp. 124-132 reproduced

E. Sayre, *Bulletin of The Museum of Fine Arts*,
Boston, LVI, no. 305, 1958, pp. 116-129 reproduced

Archivo Español de Arte, XXXII, no 128,
October 1959, no. 82 reproduced

H. Joachim, "Notes on Some Recently Acquired
Drawings," *The Art Institute of Chicago Quarterly*,
LIII, no. 2, 1959, pp. 22-27 reproduced

Connoisseur, CXLIV, no. 580, November 1959,
p. 138 reproduced

Gazette des Beaux-Arts, LVII, no. 1105, February
1961, supplement p. 41 reproduced

P. Gassier and J. Wilson, *The Life and Complete
Work of Francisco Goya*, III, New York, 1971,
nos. 1399-1400 reproduced

J. Gudiol, *Goya 1746-1828*, Barcelona, 1971,
no. 869 reproduced

Exhibitions:
1963 Wildenstein, no. 121 reproduced

After the severe illness which befell Goya early
in 1793, and left him almost deaf in his mid-forties
when he was at the height of his success as a
portrait painter and designer of tapestries, he became a trenchant philosophical observer of society
instead of the happy participant he had been before. The culmination of these observations was the
set of eighty etchings, *Los Caprichos,* which he
published in 1799. Instead of leaving his imagination exhausted, this gigantic effort rather provided
a stimulus to continue in this same vein, for there
are no fewer than eight albums which can be
partially reconstructed from surviving individual
pages (cf. E. A. Sayre, op. cit., pp. 130 ff.). At
least two of these albums still seem to be concurrent
with the *Caprichos,* but the others are later.

The Dancing Girl (*"Cuydado con ese paso"*)
is no. 30 of the "Dark Border Set" (called 'Album
E' by Miss Sayre), of which about twenty-four
pages seem to have survived, barely half, considering that '49' is the highest occurring number.

Thus it is difficult to judge the tenor of the
entire set, but some of the single figure pieces deal
with the ambitions and follies of the very young
and the very old.

Rarely has Goya portrayed the carefree exuber-
ance of youth more charmingly than in this drawing of a young dancer with a radiantly happy face,
yet the ominous inscription warns us that grief is
not far from happiness. Some of the highlights on
the darkest part of the garment are scratched in, a
highly unorthodox but very effective method. The
reverse of the drawing shows an unfinished sketch
of a dancer in a less complicated and rather more
conventional attitude. Unfortunately, the sheets
bearing the numbers closest to ours are not known
at present.

Cuydado con ese paso

23 *The Goatherd Lamon Handing the Infant Daphnis to his Wife Myrtele* Inscribed: *Abraham Bloemaert f.* in lower right by a later hand in different ink

Pen and brown ink with grey wash, heightened with white, over graphite on pinkish paper; strips of paper added on all sides.
267 x 374 mm   1973.154

Collections:

J.B. de Graaf, Amsterdam (Lugt 1120)

Acquired from William H. Schab, New York

Flemish by birth, Dubois is reported to have come to live in France at the age of twenty-five. Little is known about him until 1606, when he was appointed painter to Marie de' Medici. At Fontainebleau, he decorated the Queen's apartment with scenes from the story of Clorinda, the Galerie de Diane, and other rooms. Although his work is strongly influenced by the Italian masters who participated in the decoration of the palace (particularly Primaticcio), there remains a Netherlandish Mannerist trend which later caused some confusion with Bloemaert, who was immensely popular in eighteenth-century France.

Dubois drawings are rare, and the first serious study on them was written by Sylvie Beguin of the Louvre ("Dessins d'Ambroise Dubois", *L'Oeil,* cxxxv, 1966, pp. 6-15, 67; see also the same author's "Quelques nouveaux dessins d'Ambroise Dubois", *Revue de L'Art,* xiv, 1971, pp. 31-38, as well as pages 81-89 of the exhibition catalogue *L'Ecole de Fontainebleau,* Paris, Grand Palais, 1972-73). Mme Beguin has not only confirmed the attribution of our drawing, but has also identified the subject.

She has published three other drawings obviously by the same hand and in the same lively and graceful manner depicting scenes from Daphnis and Chloe, the Greek pastoral attributed to Longus, which after its French translation by Amyot in 1559 inspired so much of French art, literature, and music for centuries to come. One of these drawings (Beguin, 1971, fig. 6) shows the same false signature of Bloemaert, and as both drawings were once owned by the same eighteenth-century Dutch collector, it is possible that he so signed them.

49

Daniel Dumoustier   Paris 1574 - 1646

24 *Portrait of Cardinal de la Rochefoucauld*
Inscribed: *Le Cardinal de la Rochefoucault* 1624
Red and black chalk on white paper
434 x 338 mm   1959.35
Collections:
Acquired from Wildenstein, New York
Publications:
The Art Institute of Chicago Annual Report
1958-1959, p. 33 reproduced
Art Quarterly, XXII, no. 4, Winter 1959, p. 396
reproduced
Exhibitions:
1963 Wildenstein, New York, *Master Drawings
from The Art Institute of Chicago* (hereafter cited
as "1963 Wildenstein"), no. 34 reproduced

Daniel Dumoustier was a member of a family of
portrait painters which can be traced from the early
sixteenth well into the eighteenth century. Though
the major part of his activity falls into the seventeenth century, he was unaffected by contemporary
Italian portraiture and remained faithful to the old-
fashioned tradition established by François Clouet
and continued by the senior members of his own
clan. It is a portrait of respectful distance and
courtly reserve, yet not without power of characterization. Bishop of Clermont and Senlis, Grand
Almoner of France, La Rochefoucauld was appointed Cardinal in 1607. Born in 1558, he was in
his middle sixties when Dumoustier drew his
portrait. He died in 1645 at the age of eighty-seven.
It was mainly due to his insistence that Henry IV
became converted to Catholicism before his coronation. As French Ambassador to the Pope, the
Cardinal upheld the ancient rights of the Most
Christian King and the Gallican Church against
encroachment by Rome.

The coarse execution of letters and date at the
top is very similar to the inscriptions of the large
majority of the Dumoustier portraits in the Louvre.
It is probably a seventeenth-century hand, but
certainly not the artist's own.

LE CARDINAL DE LA   ROCHEFOUCAULT

1624

25   *The Holy Family Resting on the Flight into Egypt*
Inscribed: *J. de Bellange* (probably the artist's signature)

Pen and wash in brown ink with touches of white over black chalk on ivory paper
240 x 200 mm   1967.17
Watermark: Bird and star

Collections:
Berkeley Sheffield, Doncaster

Louis Deglatigny (Lugt 1768a)
Sale: Paris, June 14-15, 1937, no. 45

Maurice Gobin, Paris (Lugt 1124 a/b)

Dr. Ludwig Burchard, London

Acquired from Slatkin, New York

Publications:
F. Pariset, "Dessins de Jacques de Bellange,"
La Critica d'Arte, January 1950, pp 341-355 reproduced

Art Quarterly, 1967, p. 66 reproduced p. 76

Exhibitions:
1966 New York, Charles E. Slatkin Gallery,
Selected Drawings, no. 20 reproduced

1972 Toronto, Art Gallery of Ontario, *French Master Drawings of the 17th and 18th Centuries in North American Collections,* no. 4 reproduced

Jacques Bellange is one of many rediscoveries of the twentieth century. He was born, lived, and died in Nancy, which until its capture in 1633 by Louis XIII held considerable importance as the capital of the Dukes of Lorraine. Most of his paintings seem to have perished, but forty-six etchings and a number of drawings attest to his extravagantly personal brand of Mannerism derived from the School of Fontainebleau and such Dutch artists as Spranger and Goltzius. Honored in his lifetime, his art was detested throughout the nineteenth century. Basan called him *"mauvais peintre et encore plus mauvais graveur"* and Robert Dumesnil in 1841 almost apologized for including him in *Le Peintre-Graveur Français.* With the modern concept of Mannerism as a movement with its own aesthetic principles, not as an aberration, Bellange has become almost a vogue. The graceful elegance of the figures and the brilliant chiaroscuro effect of the brown wash are trademarks of the artist's mature style, although the scarcity of his drawings impedes the establishment of a plausible chronology.

53

26   *The Old Savoyard*
Red and black chalk on ivory paper
360 x 224 mm   1964.74

Collections:

Jean de Julienne   Sale: Paris,
March 30-May 22, 1767, no. 769

Mrs. A. L. Grimaldi Sale: London,
February 25, 1948, no. 85 reproduced

Mrs. Corina Kavanagh, Buenos Aires
Sale: London, Sotheby & Co.,
March 11, 1964, no. 220 reproduced

Acquired at the 1964 Sotheby Sale

Publications:

E. de Goncourt, *Catalogue raisonné de l'oeuvre
peint, dessiné et gravé d'Antoine Watteau,* Paris,
1875, no. 370

K. T. Parker and J. Mathey, *Antoine Watteau,
Catalogue complet de son Oeuvre dessiné,* I, Paris,
1957, no. 492 reproduced

Art Quarterly, xxvii, No. 4, 1964, p. 499
reproduced p. 503

H. Edwards, "Two Drawings by Antoine Watteau,"
Museum Studies, I, Chicago, 1966,
pp. 8-14 reproduced

E. Munhall, "Savoyards in French 18th Century
Art," *Apollo,* February 1968, pp. 86-94 reproduced

Exhibitions:

1972, Toronto, Art Gallery of Ontario, *French
Master Drawings of the 17th and 18th Centuries in
North American Collections,* no. 153 reproduced

Watteau, acclaimed as the master of elegance in
his *fêtes galantes,* never forgot his humble origin.
Therefore, the picturesque types of the streets of
Paris were not curiosities but very real people to
him, as were beggars to Rembrandt. It is a pity
that one does not know more about the old
Savoyard, the subject of our drawing and probably
three others (Parker & Mathey, 493, 494, 495),
a hardy character with a shrewd, humorous face,
who carries his big picture box (which in the
drawing 494 he has opened, ready to tell his stories)
along with a smaller box undoubtedly containing
the marmot, the Savoyard's inseparable companion.
The very free and broad execution of this drawing
indicates thorough knowledge of Rembrandt's chalk
drawings and points to the later years of Watteau's
short life, perhaps not earlier than 1715. The drawing has been etched by Boucher in *Figures de
Différents Charactères, de Paysages, et d'Etudes
Dessinées d'Apres Nature,* Paris, 1725-28, Vol. I,
plate 22. (cf. Paul Mantz, *Cent Dessins de
Watteau Gravés par Boucher,* Paris, 1892, no 9).

55

27   *Three Studies of Seated Women*
Black, red and white chalk on grey-brown paper
260 x 370 mm   1958.8

Collections:

Earl Spencer (Lugt 1530)
Sale: London, 1811, no. 822

Edward Coxe   Sale: London,
April 13-15, 1815, no. 132

William Esdaile (Lugt 2617)
Sale: London, June 24, 1840, no. 1242

Miss James   Sale: London, Christie's,
June 22-23, 1891, no. 338

H. H. A. Josse   Sale: Paris, Galerie Georges Petit,
May 28-29, 1894, no. 45 reproduced

Camille Groult, Paris

J. Groult

P. Bordeaux-Groult

Acquired from Wildenstein, New York

Publications:

E. de Goncourt, *Catalogue raisonné de l'oeuvre
peint, dessiné et gravé d'Antoine Watteau*, Paris,
1875, no. 50

K. T. Parker and J. Mathey, *Antoine Watteau,
Calalogue complet de son Oeuvre dessiné,* II, Paris,
1957, no. 831 reproduced

The Art Institute of Chicago Annual Report,
1958-1959 reproduced on cover

Exhibitions:

1955 New York, Wildenstein, *Timeless Master
Drawings,* no. 106 reproduced on cover

1959 Baltimore, Baltimore Museum of Art, *Age of
Elegance, The Rococo and its Effect,*
no. 79 reproduced

1963 Wildenstein, no. 43 reproduced

The informality of this elegantly composed study
sheet is emphasized by the uncorrected *pentimenti*
of the woman's head at the left. Such sheets served
as source material for Watteau to draw upon whenever needed. Thus the woman with the book of
music at the left appears (with differences) in
L'Accord Parfait (E. Dacier & A. Vuaflart, *Jean
de Jullienne et les Graveurs de Watteau,* Paris,
1921, pl. 23), and the guitar-playing woman in the
center appears in *Le Bal Champêtre* (ibid. pl. 311).
But these composite drawings are not just study
sheets but works of art in their own right and they
never cease to surprise and delight by their inexhaustible variety and sense of balance. This sheet
is probably an early example of Watteau's use of
the three-chalks method, with black still dominating
as the key of the composition.

28 *Landscape with a Castle*
Inscribed: *Vataux* (not in the artist's hand)
Red chalk on ivory paper
224 x 339 mm   1964.194

Collections:
Charles Rogers, London (Lugt 624)
William Cotton
William Cotton II
Fauchier-Magnan   Sale: London, Sotheby & Co.,
December 4, 1935, no. 72 reproduced
Acquired from Slatkin, New York

Publications:
K. T. Parker and J. Mathey, *Antoine Watteau,
Catalogue complet de son Oeuvre dessiné,* I, Paris,
1957, no.427 reproduced

Art Quarterly, XXVII, 1964, p. 499 reproduced

H. Edwards, "Two Drawings by Antoine Watteau",
Museum Studies, I, 1966, pp. 8-14 reproduced

M. P. Eidelberg, "Watteau's Use of Landscape
Drawings", *Master Drawings,* v, no. 2, 1967,
pp. 173-182 reproduced

M. Cormack, *The Drawings of Watteau,* London/
New York/Sydney/Toronto, 1970 reproduced

Exhibitions:
1925 Paris, Petit Palais, *Exposition du Le Paysage
Français de Poussin à Corot,* no. 712

Only great talents can absorb many different in-
fluences and come out with their individuality
strengthened rather than weakened. This happened
to Watteau when he immersed himself with a
passion in the huge and important drawing collection of Baron Crozat, in whose house he was a
guest for several years. Among the drawings which
intrigued Watteau were numerous sixteenth-century
landscape drawings in pen and ink of the Venetian
School, probably mainly by Domenico Campagnola,
all of which he copied—or rather interpreted—in
his own favorite medium of red chalk. In some
instances, both the Campagnola original and the
Watteau copy have survived (Walter Baker Collection in New York), but in our case the original
is not known at the present time.

VATAUX

59

29   *Portrait of Mme Chardin*
Inscribed: *Chardin* 1776
Pastel on paper backed by canvas
455 x 375 mm   1962.137
Collections:
Jean-Louis David, Paris   Sale: Paris, March 18-19, 1868, no. 12
de Loriol, Geneva
Marquis de Biron, Paris
Forsyth Wickes, Newport, Rhode Island
Acquired from Wildenstein, New York
Publications:
G. P. F. Grappe, *Amour de l'Art,* XVI, no. 7, July 1935, p. 241 reproduced
H. Furst, *Connoisseur,* CVI, no. 467, 19 August 1940, p. 17 reproduced
The Art Institute of Chicago Quarterly, LVI, no. 4, Winter 1962/63, reproduced on cover
J. Vallery-Radot, *French Drawings,* N. Y., 1964, reproduced pl. 36
G. Wildenstein, *Chardin* (rev. D. Wildenstein) N. Y. 1969, no. 374 reproduced
Exhibitions:
1926 New York, Wildenstein Galleries, *J.B.S. Chardin,* No. II reproduced
1935-36 New York, The Metropolitan Museum of Art, *French Painting and Sculpture of the* XVIII *Century,* no. 26 reproduced
1952 Pittsburgh, Carnegie Institute, *French Painting* 1100-1900, no. 86 reproduced
1954 Baltimore Museum of Art, *Man and his Years,* no. 84
1956 New Haven, Conn., Yale University Art Gallery, *Pictures Collected by Yale Alumni,* no. 194
1961 Richmond, Virginia, Museum of Fine Arts, *Treasures in America,* p. 68
1963 Wildenstein, no. 46 reproduced

Chardin lost his first wife in 1735, and in 1744 married Françoise-Marguérite Pouget, a widow in comfortable circumstances. Perhaps she is the lady seen in such genre pictures as the *Pleasures of the Home* (Wildenstein, op. cit., no. 221, fig. 105) of about 1746, and the *Lady with Bird-Song Organ* (ibid. no. 227/228, fig. 109/110) of 1751, but no actual portrait seems to exist before 1775. By 1771 the aging artist had developed an aversion to the smell of oil paint and began making portraits in pastel. The Louvre portrait of Mme Chardin is dated 1775, and was exhibited at the Salon in the same year (ibid. no. 373, pl. 58). As he did so often before, Chardin made a replica of it the following year, losing none of the freshness and immediacy by doing it the second time.

30   *Boy Holding a Carrot*
Inscribed: *F. Boucher* 1738
Pastel on buff paper
308 x 243 mm   1971.22

Collections:
Antoine Joseph Dezallier d'Argenville
Sale: Paris, 1766, no. 72

Randon de Boisset Sale: Paris, February 27,
1777, no 201

Bruun-Neergard Sale: August 30, 1814, no. 45

Private collection, Cher-et-Loire Sale: Paris,
Palais Galliéra, December 7, 1970, no. 1

Acquired from Slatkin, New York

Publications:
E. and J. de Goncourt, *L'Art du dix-huitième
siècle* I, Paris 1880, p. 201

Andre Michel, *François Boucher,* Paris [1906],
no. 2395

Art News, LXIX, no. 8, December 1970,
p. 53 reproduced

Antiques, CI, no. 3, March 1972, p. 474 reproduced

The Art Institute of Chicago Annual Report
1970-71, p. 12, color reproduced on cover

Exhibitions:
1974 National Gallery of Art, Washington, and
The Art Institute of Chicago, *François Boucher in
North American Collections: 100 Drawings*
(hereafter cited as "1974 Washington") cat. no. 32,
illus., color fronts.

In 1737, Quentin de La Tour, the great specialist of pastel portraits, scored a popular success at the Salon du Louvre with a self-portrait and a portrait of Madame Boucher. This may have induced Boucher to work in that medium also—at least, no pastels by his hand before 1738 seem to be known, and this irresistibly charming and alive portrait of a boy could well be one of his earliest essays in this medium. It is interesting to note that a boy seated on the ground and holding a carrot appears in at least two paintings of pastoral scenes by Boucher (cf. exhibition 1963 Finch College Museum of Art, *French Masters,* reproduced on cover). Connected with these paintings is a preliminary drawing (A. Ananoff, *L'Oeuvre Dessiné de François Boucher,* Paris 1966, no. 537, fig. 99).

63

31 *A Valet Serving Chocolate*
Red, black and white chalk over pencil on buff paper
Watermark: Bunch of Grapes and initials HP (?)
345 x 195 mm   1959.183
Collections:
Louis-Pierre-Martin Norblin de la Gourdaine
Madame la Baronne de Connantre
Baronne de Ruble
Madame de Witte
Marquise de Bryas
M. Cailleux, Paris
Acquired from Slatkin, New York
Publications:
E. and J. de Goncourt, *L'Art du Dix-Huitième Siècle* I, Paris, 1880, p. 199
A. Michel, *François Boucher,* Paris, [1906], no. 1279
Art Quarterly, XXIII, no. 1, Spring 1960, p. 110 reproduced
Galerie Cailleux, *François Boucher,* Paris, 1964, mentioned under no. 17
V. Carlson, "Three Drawings by François Boucher", *Master Drawings,* IV, no. 2, 1966, pp. 157-163 reproduced
Exhibitions:
1963 Wildenstein, no. 47
1974 Washington, cat. no. 36, illus.

The abundance of undistinguished drawings, which issued from Boucher's *atelier* in his later years, hurt his reputation in the nineteenth and twentieth centuries. To understand his great qualities as a draughtsman, we should turn to those drawings which are clearly preparatory for his major paintings. Often they are not signed, although that should not be considered a rule. The drawing of a valet is a splendid example of the refreshingly vigorous style of his early maturity. It is a study for one of his rare oils of domestic scenes, *Le Déjeuner en Famille* (or *L'Interieur de Famille*) of 1739 in the Louvre, which presumably shows Madame Boucher with her two small children and another young woman at their two o'clock repast in an elegantly furnished room of the artist's home. The valet is hidden from the waist down by the seated woman feeding the little boy Juste-Nathan (born in 1736). Madame Boucher at the right side looks down at her small daughter, Jeanne-Elisabeth-Victoire (born in 1735), with her assortment of toys. A preparatory drawing for Madame Boucher in the Liechtenstein Collection was once believed to be by Chardin (Albertina facsimiles II, no. 131). Another study for the same figure is in the Hermitage.

François Boucher

32 *Wooded Landscape with Boy Fishing*
Black and white chalk on blue paper
300 x 443 mm   1960.206
Collections:
Jean Gigoux, Paris
Marquis de Fourquevaulx, Paris
Delestre, Sale Paris, April 18-30, 1876, no. 276
Acquired from Wildenstein, New York
Publications:
Goncourt, E. and J. de, *L'Art du Dix-Huitième
Siècle,* 1, p. 208, Paris, 1880
A. Michel, *François Boucher,* Paris 1906, no. 1950
V. Carlson, "Three Drawings by François Boucher",
Master Drawings, IV, no. 2, 1966,
pp. 157-163 reproduced
C. O. Baer, *Landscape Drawings,* New York, 1973,
no. 105 reproduced
Exhibitions:
1963 Wildenstein, no. 48 reproduced
1974 Washington, cat. no. 57

Boucher's interest in landscape was stimulated by the frequent trips through the countryside which he had to make when, in 1734, he became associated with the tapestry workshops in Beauvais. Some of his landscape drawings, especially those with black and white chalks on blue paper, are finished works of art and hardly intended as sketches for paintings. However, at least once the same composition appears in a drawing and a painting, *Paysage pres de Beauvais:* the drawing is in Amsterdam, the painting in Leningrad. Two of the drawings on blue paper are companion pieces, being very similar in style, technique and size. Both were etched by Pierre Quentin Chédel (1705-1763) and the prints were offered for sale in *Le Mercure de France* in April of 1753. They are *Le Pêcheur* and *Le Pont Rustique* in the Albertina (J. Meder, *Albertina-Facsimile, Handzeichnungen Französischer Meister des XVI-XVIII Jahrhunderts,* Vienna, 1922, P. 30. According to an eighteenth-century inscription on an old mount, the Albertina drawing offers a view of the park of Arcueil, where Oudry also used to draw. In *Le Pêcheur* the engraver added two lines from Virgil's *Eclogue* III, which tells of a teasing game of love between Galatea and the young poet. This was probably the publisher's idea, for if Boucher had entertained any such thought he surely would have made the most of it.

In spite of the decorative scheme to which Boucher's landscapes conform, there is often a surprisingly intimate rapport with nature. In our drawing, the suggestion of a balmy, placid day is perfectly realized. The farthest group of trees seem to retreat into the soft haze of atmosphere, and we almost sense the pungent odor of decaying and growing vegetation beside the stagnant water.

Another drawing of the same scenery, but with different figures and less detail in the foreground, appeared at a Colnaghi exhibition, April 2-May 25, 1966, no 44 reproduced.

67

François Boucher

33 *Landscape with Rustic Cottage*
Black chalk on ivory paper
315 x 470 mm   1966.25
Exhibitions:
1974 Washington, cat. no. 58 reproduced

It is in drawings of this type that Boucher's knowledge and admiration of seventeenth century Dutch artists, such as Anthonie Waterloo, is most apparent. This realistic view of a ramshackle farmyard was undoubtedly drawn from nature, or at least, is a composite of smaller sketches taken on the artist's trips through the countryside.

François Boucher

34 *A Nymph: Study for Apollo and Issa*
Red, black and white chalk and estompe
on buff paper
320 x 450 mm   1967.231
Collections:
David-Weill, Paris

Barbara Hutton

John Goelet

Acquired from Slatkin, New York
Publications:
A. Michel, *François Boucher,* Paris, 1906, no. 82
Société de Reproduction des Dessins de Maîtres, v,
Paris, 1913 reproduced

G. Henriot, "La Collection David-Weill,"
Amour de l'Art, vi, no. 1, January 1925, p. 9
Collection David-Weill, iii, Paris, 1928,
p. 31 reproduced

B. Lossky, "L'Apollon et Isse dans l'Oeuvre de
François Boucher," *Gazette des Beaux-Arts,*
November 1954, p. 238 reproduced
Exhibitions:
1938 New York, Wildenstein & Co., *French
XVIIIth Century Pastels, Watercolors and
Drawings from the David-Weill Collection,* no. 53

1974 Washington, cat. no. 66 reproduced

This composition is a preparatory drawing for the group of two nymphs in the lower left corner of *Apollo and Issa,* a painting of 1750 in the Musée des Beaux Arts in Tours, which certainly is one of the artist's major efforts in mythology. But not even Boucher could sustain in the painting the exceptionally graceful rhythm of line in the body of the nymph, which makes this one of his finest drawings of a nude.

71

François Boucher

35 *Study for a Triton in Le Lever du Soleil*
Black, white and red chalk and estompe
on buff paper
220 x 270 mm   1965.240
Collections:
Charles-Emile Picard, Paris
Acquired from Jacques Seligmann, New York
Exhibitions:
1974 Washington, cat. no. 69 reproduced

This vigorous drawing is a study for the triton—not yet holding the conch shell—in the painting *Sunrise*. The two paintings, *Sunrise* and *Sunset,* both in the Wallace Collection, were made as tapestry designs about 1748. The Goncourt brothers described them as "le plus grand effort du peintre, les deux grandes machines de son oeuvre." In the final version, the bulging muscles of the triton's powerful back are hidden by the dimpled arm of a nereid. Boucher had learned from Rubens how to handle such contrasts with virtuosity. An equally forceful study for a triton in the *Sunset* uses the same muscular model (Ananoff, *L'Oeuvre Dessiné de François Boucher,* Paris, 1966, no. 904, fig. 155). Another drawing after the same model (Wallace Collection, reproduced in *Apollo,* no. 35, May 1942, p. 109) is a study for the triton just above the lower left corner in the *Sunrise*. It would seem that Boucher insisted on the model's hair being wet in these studies. The list of drawings for the *Sunrise* could easily be enlarged, and we will only mention here the magnificent study for Apollo himself in the David Daniels Collection, New York (*Drawings from the David Daniels Collection,* Cambridge, Mass., 1968, no. 22, reproduced)

73

François Boucher

36   *Domestic Scene: Mother with Two Small Children*
Before a Mantelpiece
Black chalk
223 x 183 mm   1960.842
Collections:
Jean Masson (Lugt 1494a)   Sale: Geneva, N.
Rauch, June 13-14, 1960, no 43 reproduced
Acquired from Slatkin, New York
Publications:
International Studio, LXXVII, no. 316, September
1923, p. 480 reproduced

The subject occurs in many versions in Boucher's
work in different degrees of execution. This sheet
is a superb example of the artist's swiftest manner,
in which he still managed to clearly articulate every
element of the composition. Such a sheet would
naturally attract a sophisticated drawing collector
as Jean Masson (1865-1933).

37 *Eros and Psyche: Design for a Ceiling*
Pen and brown wash over black and red chalk on
ivory paper
240 x 315 mm (oval)   1960.357
Collections:
Jean Dubois, Paris   Sale: Paris, Georges Petit,
March 21-22, 1927, no. 4 reproduced
Marius Paulme, Paris   Sale: Paris, Georges Petit,
May 13, 1929, no. 19 reproduced
Monsieur X, Paris   Sale: Geneva, N. Rauch,
June 13-15, 1960, no. 44 reproduced
Publications:
A. Ananoff, *Les Dessins de Boucher* 1703-1770, I,
Paris, 1966, no. 868 reproduced
V. Carlson, "Three Drawings by
François Boucher," *Master Drawings,* IV, no. 2,
1966, pp. 157-163 reproduced
Exhibitions:
1963 Wildenstein, no. 49
1974 Washington, cat. no. 55 reproduced

The dynamic swirl of lines combined with the brilliant chiaroscuro effect contained within the oval
shape, make this drawing an unsurpassed example
of Boucher's spontaneous genius for decoration. It
seems that the composition was not used for any
actual ceiling. The Abbé Saint-Non effectively
copied it in aquatint in 1766.

38   *Poodle Surprising a Swan on her Nest*
Signed: *Oudry fecit, pour présent*
Grey wash heightened with white on blue paper
320 x 410 mm   1966.351
Collections:
Edmond et Jules de Goncourt (Lugt 1089)
Sale: Paris, Hotel Drouot, February 15-17,
1897, no. 216

Marquise de la Ferronnays

Private collection, Paris

Acquired from Slatkin, New York

Publications:
Marquis de Chennevières, *Les Dessins de Maîtres
Anciens Exposés à l'Ecole des Beaux-Arts en* 1879,
Paris, 1880, p. 99

J. Locquin, "Catalogue Raisonné de l'Oeuvre de
Jean-Baptiste Oudry," *Archives de l'Art Français,*
VI, Paris, 1912, no. 614

J. Vergnet-Ruiz, "Oudry," *Les Peintres Français du*
XVIII *e Siècle,* II, Paris/Brussels, 1930, no. 54

H. N. Opperman, "Some Animal Drawings by
Jean-Baptiste Oudry," *Master Drawings,* IV, no. 4,
1966, pp. 384-409 reproduced

Exhibitions:
1879 Paris, Ecole des Beaux-Arts,
Dessins de Maîtres Anciens, no. 489

1958 Stockholm, Nationalmuseum,
Fem Sekler Fransk Konst, no. 238

1966 New York, Charles E. Slatkin Galleries,
Selected Drawings, no. 22 reproduced

Oudry's own inscription classifies this masterful
brush drawing as a presentation piece, and as such
it probably is a replica rather than a study for the
painting which hangs in the Swedish Embassy in
Paris (cf. Opperman, op. cit., fig. 9). Another
replica of this painting is in a private collection in
London. In the drawing, the hunting poodle blends
even more with the swamp foliage than in the
painting. In the era of Louis XV, Oudry was the
unequalled painter of animal life, and the King
commissioned him to do portraits of his favorite
dogs in his presence. The subject was repeated in
a Sèvres biscuit group in The Walters Art Gallery,
Baltimore (this information we owe to Mr. Richard
H. Randall, Jr., Director, The Walters Art Gallery).

79

39   *Two Small Girls*
Red chalk
200 x 244 mm (sheet)   1971.527
Collections:
See remarks at right
Acquired from Adolphe Stein, Paris
(6 drawings 1971.527-532)

This exquisite drawing is a study for the two small girls in the foreground of the painting in Dresden, *The Dance Between the Two Fountains* (G. Wildenstein, *Lancret,* Paris, 1924, no. 143, fig. 41)

40   *Young Woman with a Watering Jug*
Black, white and red chalks on grey paper
260 x 137 mm   1971.532

This and the following drawing are similar in their very free and summary execution. Both are connected with *Spring,* first of a series of four paintings which were engraved by N. de Larmessin and shown at the Salon of 1745 (Wildenstein, no. 15, fig. 14). Instead of the bird cage, the girl is now holding a flower basket. However, there is a painting in the Louvre, *The Cage,* where a very similar figure of a girl appears, holding a bird cage, and looking at her lover with the same amorous expression as in our drawing (ibid. no. 460, fig. 116).

41   *Young Woman with a Bird Cage*
Black, white and red chalk on grey paper
280 x 185 mm   1971.531
Exhibitions:
1972, Toronto, Art Gallery of Ontario, *French Master Drawings of the 17th and 18th Centuries in North American Collections,* no. 74, p. 173, reproduced Pl. 74. Catalogue by Pierre Rosenberg.

Lancret met Watteau in the *atelier* of Gillot, and the two artists became friends until Watteau took offense at the younger man's rather close imitations of his own work. Lancret was guilty of this at times, but to regard him merely as a clever imitator of Watteau would be a grave injustice. Lancret's view of society is seldom as idealized and sublimated as Watteau's, and he sometimes displays a ribald Hogarthian streak—as in the *Ham Luncheon* (*Partie de Plaisir,* Wildenstein, op. cit., no. 73, pl. 28). In his drawings, too, he shows an individual profile quite different from Watteau's. He likes short, energetic, angular strokes, rarely the soft and subtle modelling of forms and textures found with the older master. The six sheets (one double-sided) discussed here are all connected with paintings or engravings after lost paintings, and their interesting history dates back to eighteenth-century Potsdam and the entourage of Frederick II of Prussia, who was Lancret's best customer, having bought no fewer than twenty-six paintings. The drawings are known to have been owned by three generations of one family, beginning with Andreas Ludwig Krüger (1743-1822), architect, painter, and etcher in Potsdam. At the age of nine, he came to live with his uncle, Andreas Krüger, also an architect, who collaborated with G. W. Knobelsdorff, the King's chief architect and artistic adviser. Andreas Krüger inherited much of Knobelsdorff's estate in works of art (cf. Thieme-Becker), so that it is likely that the Lancret drawings once were owned by Knobelsdorff who undoubtedly had been instrumental in the King's acquisition of Lancret's paintings. From A. L. Krüger, the drawings passed on to his son, Carl (1776-1828). Curiously, however, he listed the drawings as being by Watteau, which is proof how information can get lost within one family in three generations.

40 Nicolas Lancret
Young Woman with a Watering Jug

41 Nicolas Lancret
Young Woman with a Bird Cage

Nicolas Lancret

42 *Two Studies of a Guitar Player in Turkish Costume*
(Le Turc Amoureux)
Red chalk
220 x 310 mm   1971.530

The figure at the right was used twice, the first
time in a painting (Wildenstein, no. 688, fig. 169),
which is a companion piece for *La Belle Grècque*
(ibid. fig. 170), and the second time as a wall
decoration in the house of M. de Boullongne on
the Place Vendôme, now in the Musée des Arts
Décoratifs, Paris (ibid. fig. 184).

Nicolas Lancret

43   *Old Woman Seated, Drapery Study, and*
Head of Another Old Woman
Black and white chalk on grey paper
Verso: *Young Woman in Dancing Stance* (c 1732)
Red and white chalk
168 x 246 mm   1971.529

Both old women occur in Lancret's painting *Old Age* in the National Gallery, London (Wildenstein, no. 33, fig. 22), which also owns the three com-

panion pieces, *Childhood, Adolescence,* and *Youth.* They were certainly painted before July 30, 1735, on which date N. de Larmessin gave to the Academy engravings he had made after them (cf. ibid. p. 73).

The dancing figure on the reverse is a study for *The Dance Between the Pavilion and the Fountain,* at the New Palace in Potsdam (Wildenstein, no. 152, fig. 51, once owned by Frederick II. This painting is signed and dated 1732).

Nicolas Lancret

44 *Young Woman Standing, Hand on Hip*
Black chalk
280 x 185 mm   1971.528

This drawing, executed in bold strokes, is a study
for the woman standing at the right in the *Bird
Catchers* in the Wallace Collection (*La Chasse à la
Pipée*, Wildenstein, no. 462, fig. 118).

89

Nicolas Lancret

45   *Young Man Standing*
Inscribed: *Gillet de l'Opera* in red ink
Black chalk
203 x 105 mm   1966.352

Collections:
E. Joseph-Rignault, Paris (Lugt 2218 and S. 2218, mentions this drawing at the sale of May 26, 1937)
Acquired from Richard H. Zinser, New York

No direct connection with a known painting can be established, but similar attitudes occur in many Lancret paintings, for example *The Dance Before The Tent* (Wildenstein, no. 151, fig. 50).

Gillet de l'opera. Rig.

46   *Self-Portrait*
Pastel on greenish paper
324 x 240 mm   1959.242
Collections:
Carrier, Paris   Sale: Paris, 1875, no. 10
Mme Becq de Fouquières, Paris, 1925
David-Weill, Paris
Acquired from French and Co., New York
Publications:
Gazette des Beaux-Arts, II, Paris 1908,
p. 7 reproduced
E. Fleury and B. Brière, *Catalogue des Pastels de
M. Quentin de La Tour,* 1920, pp. 32-33, no. A
L'Amour de l'Art, VI, January 1925, p. II reproduced
Collection David-Weill, II, Paris, 1927, pp. 25-26
reproduced
A. Besnard and G. Wildenstein, *Latour,* Paris,
1928, no. 246 reproduced
Art News, XXXVII, no. 6, Nov. 5, 1938
reproduced on cover
E. Fleury and G. Brière, *Collection Maurice
Quentin de La Tour,* 1954, p. 33 no. A. II
H. Edwards, "Two Drawings by Maurice Quentin
de La Tour," *The Art Institute of Chicago
Quarterly,* LV, no. 1, March 1961,
pp. 2-4 reproduced on cover
Exhibitions:
1908 Paris, Georges Petit, *Les Maîtres de 18ème
Siècle: Cent Pastels,* no. 29
1938 New York, Wildenstein & Co., *French XVIII
Century—Pastels, Watercolors and Drawings from
the David-Weill Collection,* no. 8
1963 Wildenstein, no. 50 reproduced

Without the portraits of Maurice Quentin de La
Tour, the aura of eighteenth-century France would
be much less alive for us today. He portrayed
almost all of the political, social and intellectual
leaders of the time from Louis XV and Madame de
Pompadour to Jean-Jacques Rousseau, Diderot, and
Voltaire, with a degree of *verité* that astounded his
contemporaries as much as it impresses later generations. From 1737 to 1773 he exhibited at the Salon
du Louvre nearly every year with unfailing success.
As already mentioned in the entry for the Boucher
pastel, his pieces shown in 1737 were a self-portrait
and a portrait of Madame Boucher. The self-portrait
exists in several versions (Besnard & Wildenstein,
nos. 212-215, figs. 1-5) probably not all authentic.
The Art Institute self-portrait shows only the face
itself; a cap is lightly outlined, which does not
necessarily imply that it is unfinished, as the unfinished look is sometimes an intentional effect in
the eighteenth century. The actual age of the artist
cannot be told with certainty, but it must be fairly
close to that of the 1737 portrait.

47 *Portrait of an Elderly Man*
Black and white chalk touched with blue and red
pastel on brown paper
300 x 250 mm   1958.543

Collections:

Camille Groult, Paris

Acquired from Wildenstein, New York

Publications:

A. Besnard and G. Wildenstein, *Latour,* Paris,
1928, no. 607 reproduced

Art News, LV, no. 6, October 1956, p. 6

Art Quarterly, XXII, no. 2, Summer 1959, p. 196
reproduced

H. Edwards, "Two Drawings by Maurice Quentin
de la Tour," *The Art Institute of Chicago
Quarterly,* LV, no. 1, March 1961,
pp. 2-4 reproduced

A. Frankfurter, "'Il bon disegno' from Chicago,"
Art News, LXII, no. 7, November 1963,
pp. 28-31 reproduced

Gazette des Beaux-Arts, LVII, no. 1105, February
1961, supplement p. 37 reproduced

Exhibitions:

1956 New York, Wildenstein & Co.,
For the Connoisseur, no. 20

1961 Minneapolis, University Gallery, University
of Minnesota, *The Eighteenth Century: One
Hundred Drawings by One Hundred Masters,*
no. 51

1963 Wildenstein, no. 51

The *Portrait of an Elderly Man* has been tentatively
identified as the painter Louis de Silvestre (1675-
1760), who is the subject of a large pastel by
La Tour, shown at the Salon du Louvre in 1753.
However, he also shows a certain resemblance to a
preparatory study for a portrait of Prosper Jolyot
de Crébillon (1674-1762) of the Académie Française (ibid. no 80, fig. 139). Such preparatory
studies reveal La Tour's profound understanding
of the basic structure of a face, and we have reason
to be grateful that not all of them were finished.

48   *Young Man Standing* c. 1760
Black, red and white chalk with estompe
on buff paper
507 x 290 mm   1968.461

Collections:

St. Petersburg Academy of Fine Arts
(Lugt S2699a)

Sale: Leipzig, C. G. Boerner, May 4, 1932, no. 48

Sale: London, Christie's, March 26, 1968, no. 77

Acquired from Paul Drey Gallery, New York

Publications:

F. Monod and L. Hautecoeur, *Les Dessins de
Greuze Conservés à l'Academie des Beaux-Arts de
St. Petersbourg,* Paris 1922, p. 28, no. 48

The figure of the young man is a preparatory study for the painting, *The Marriage Contract.* When it was shown in the Salon of 1761, it was acclaimed for extolling the virtues of unspoiled, honest village life, in the spirit of Diderot and Rousseau. The vigorous draughtsmanship of this sheet is a comforting contrast to the artist's innumerable sentimental red chalk drawings of female heads.

49 *Arbor with Two Children*
Inscribed: *Napoli* 1760
Red chalk on ivory paper
360 x 485 mm   1962.486

Collections:

Anonymous sale, May 29, 1884, no. 63

Alfred Beurdeley (Lugt 421)   Sale: Paris,
Georges Petit, March 13-15, 1905, no. 72

Camille Groult

Anonymous sale, Paris, Palais Galliéra, April 10-11,
1962, no. 33

Acquired from Slatkin, New York

Publications:

A. Ananoff, *L'Oeuvre Dessiné de J.-H. Fragonard,*
II, Paris, 1963, no. 959

H. Joachim, "Three Drawings by Fragonard,"
The Art Institute of Chicago Quarterly, LVI, no. 4,
Winter 1962-1963, p. 71 reproduced

C. O. Baer, *Landscape Drawings,* New York, 1973,
no. 106 reproduced

Exhibitions:

1963 Wildenstein, no. 57 reproduced

Having studied with Chardin (for only half a year), with Boucher and with Carle van Loo, Fragonard at twenty-four was well prepared for his first trip to Rome in 1756 as a student of the French Academy. Toward the end of his stay in Rome he met the Abbé Richard de Saint-Non, who commissioned him to make drawings of the scenery in and around Rome and Naples. It is doubtful, however, that this intimate nature study of a neglected corner in a park would have been intended for Saint-Non. There is a companion piece, also inscribed *Napoli* 1760 in the Palais des Beaux-Arts in Lille (Ananoff 960). Both drawings were in the sale of 1884.

50   *A Bull of the Roman Campagna*
Brown wash over black chalk on ivory paper
363 x 493 mm   1962.116

Collections:
H. Walferdin, Paris   Sale: April 12-16, 1880,
no. 195

Baronne de Ruble, Paris

Alfred Beurdeley (Lugt 421)   Sale: Paris,
Georges Petit, March 13-15, 1905,
no. 78 reproduced

Count von Moltke

William K. Vanderbilt

Princess Charles Murat, New York   Sale: London,
Sotheby & Co., November 29, 1961,
no. 29 reproduced

Acquired at the 1961 Sotheby Sale

Publications:
R. Portalis, *Honoré Fragonard, sa vie et son oeuvre,*
II, Paris, 1889, p. 200 reproduced and p. 313

A. Ananoff, *L'Oeuvre Dessiné de J.-H. Fragonard,*
I, Paris, 1961-1970, no. 280 reproduced;
II, p. 304 addenda no. 280;
III, p. 296 addenda no. 280;
IV, p. 352 addenda no. 280.

H. Joachim, "Three Drawings by Fragonard,"
The Art Institute of Chicago Quarterly, LVI, no. 4,
Winter 1962-1963, p. 70 reproduced

Exhibitions:
1879 Paris, Ecole des Beaux-Arts,
Dessins des Maîtres Anciens, no. 584

1963 Wildenstein, no. 58

1972 Toronto, Art Gallery of Ontario, *French
Master Drawings of the 17th and 18th Centuries
in North American Collections,* no. 49 reproduced

"L'oeuvre de la plus grande puissance d'expression éclatante de lumière," was the apt comment in the Beurdeley sale catalogue of 1905. The wash is applied with the greatest freedom over summary outlines in black chalk. Another version of this composition was in the David-Weill, Cassel von Doorn, and G. Wildenstein Collections (Ananoff no. 279, fig. 104).

51 *Portrait of a Young Lady*
Inscribed: *Rome* 1774
Bistre wash over graphite on ivory paper
427 x 327 mm   1960.209

Collections:
General Brunet-Denon   Sale: February 2, 1846,
no. 268

M. Mayor   Sale: November 21-22, 1859, no. 56

Publications:
R. Portalis, *Honoré Fragonard, sa vie et son oeuvre,*
II, Paris, 1889, p. 298

A. Ananoff, *L'Oeuvre Dessiné de J.-H. Fragonard,*
III, Paris, 1968, no. 1287 reproduced

P. Lamy, "Fragonard, une découverte capitale et
des inédits revelateurs," *Connaissance des Arts,*
CXII, July 1961, p. 55 reproduced

Gazette des Beaux-Arts, LVII, no. 1105, supplement
February 1961, p. 37 reproduced

H. Joachim, "Three Drawings by Fragonard,"
The Art Institute of Chicago Quarterly, LVI, no. 4,
Winter 1962-1963, p. 68 reproduced

Exhibitions:
1963 Wildenstein, no. 59 reproduced

The beautiful aristocratic face of the sitter, with
large, limpid eyes and a Grecian nose, appears again
in a drawing at Besançon (*Inventaire Général des
Dessins des Musées de Province, Collection P.-A.
Paris,* December 1957, no. 78), where it is assumed
to be a portrait of Marguerite Gérard, the artist's
sister-in-law. However, Marguerite was only 13 in
1774 and surely did not accompany Fragonard and
the wealthy financier, Bergeret de Grancourt, on
their trip to Italy 1773-75. Bergeret, on the other
hand, had a Mlle Vignier as his companion ("gou-
vernante"), who later became Madame Bergeret.
The similarity of the two portraits in Besançon and
Chicago is even more striking, as this type of face
differs so completely from the usual female face in
Fragonard's work. The identification is further complicated by the existence of a replica of this drawing
(Ananoff III, no. 1286, fig. 383) which is inscribed: *Rome* 1774/*lady*/*Cumberland*/*fragonard.*
In the latter drawing, an elaborate mantelpiece has
been added behind the sitter, the face is more
generalized and less individualized, and the handling of the wash is so totally different that there is
reason to suspect a later hand copying Fragonard.
Still a third version, again with the mantelpiece,
has been published by Jacques Wilhelm in *Bergeret
de Grancourt, Voyage d'Italie 1773-1774,* Paris 1948,
p. 60 (Ananoff 1288, not reproduced.)

52 *Marguerite Gérard Reading to Her Mother and Rosalie Fragonard*
Brown wash over pencil on white paper
Watermark: Fleur-de-lys in cartouche
330 x 404 mm   1965.454

Publications:
A. Ananoff, *L'Oeuvre Dessiné de Fragonard,* II, Paris, 1963, no. 738, p. 73, fig. 207, who lists the following provenance: Comte de Choiseul-Gauffier, Charles-Maurice de Talleyrand-Périgord, Georges Plach, Vienna (before 1865), A. de Gourmont, and S. Higgons.

Acquired from Higgons, Paris

Marguerite Gérard, her lips slighty parted in the process of reading aloud to her enraptured audience, wears the same hat and dress we see in another Art Institute drawing by the artist, *The Letter* (1942.32). Another, smaller, version of this drawing is in a private collection in Switzerland.

53   *Fire in the Port*
Inscribed: *L. M.* 1788
Gouache on ivory paper
335 x 450 mm   1964.246

Collections:
Marquis Le Franc de Pompignon, Château de
Hordesse Sale: Paris, Hotel Drouot, June 20,
1927, no. 4
Acquired from Wildenstein, New York

Publications:
Art Quarterly, XXVII, no. 4, 1964, p. 499 reproduced

Exhibitions:
1934 London, Wildenstein & Co., *French Drawings
from Clouet to Ingres,* no. 46 reproduced

1955 Now York, Wildenstein & Co.,
Timeless Master Drawings, no. 87

1956 New York, Wildenstein & Co.,
For the Connoisseur, no. 37

Louis-Gabriel Moreau

54 *Waterfall*
Inscribed: *L. M.* 1788
Gouache over pencil on ivory paper
335 x 450 mm   1964.245

Collections:
Marquis Le Franc de Pompignon, Château de
Hordesse Sale: Paris, Hotel Drouot,
June 20, 1927, no. 3
Acquired from Wildenstein, New York

Exhibitions:
1934 London, Wildenstein & Co., *French Drawings
from Clouet to Ingres,* no. 46

1952 The Minneapolis Institute of Arts,
Watercolors by The Masters: Dürer to Cézanne,
no. 25.

1955 New York, Wildenstein & Co.,
Timeless Master Drawings, no. 86

1956 New York, Wildenstein & Co.,
For the Connoisseur, no. 36

1962 Santa Barbara, Calif., Santa Barbara Museum
of Art, *Painted Papers: Watercolors from Dürer
to the Present,* no. 62

An over-all perspective of French art in the eighteenth century would be incomplete without the
landscapes of the elder Moreau. Little noticed in
his day and almost forgotten in the nineteenth
century, his unique pioneering position in the
history of French landscape painting was not really
appreciated until our century. These two sheets
are perfect examples of his free and luminous
handling of gouache.

Jean-Michel Moreau (le jeune)   Paris 1741 - 1814

55   *The Departure by Coach*
Light brown wash over black chalk on ivory paper
226 x 168 mm   1960.825

Collections:
Joseph-Ignace Guillotin, Paris
Dr. Jacob Hirsch

Publications:
E. and J. de Goncourt, *L'Art du Dix-Huitième
Siècle,* II, Paris, 1882, p. 212
R. Portalis, *Les Dessinateurs d'Illustrations au
Dix-Huitième Siècle,* II, Paris, 1877, p. 461

Exhibitions:
1963 Wildenstein, no. 64

The Goncourts and Portalis listed the drawing as having been in the collection of Dr. Guillotin, inventor of the guillotine. The composition is similar (but by no means identical) to *Les Petits Parrains,* which was engraved in 1777 by Baquoy and Patas after Moreau's design of 1776 and published as Plate 18 in the Second Suite of the *Monument du Costume.* The main difference is that the "Little Godparents", who are about to enter the coach, are children, while the corresponding figures in the drawing are adults. The text on the adjoining page in the *Monument* explicitly speaks of the children "Aurore" and "le jeune chevalier" being on their way to a church to attend a baptism. It is therefore possible that the drawing was intended for Plate 14 of the same suite, where a gentleman is escorting a lady, not to a coach, but to a sedan chair. It may be considered a prototype for both engravings. Recently, the suggestion has been made that the drawing is not by Moreau at all, but instead is a very early work by Fragonard.

56 *Studies for the Oath of the Tennis Court*
Recto: *Bailly standing on desk, asking for a vote*
Verso: *Large group voting*
Brush with black and grey ink over pencil on
ivory paper
390 x 255 mm   1960.207

Collections:
Estate of the artist   Sale: Paris, April 17, 1826,
no. 71 or 72
M. Coutan   Sale: Paris, April 17-18, 1830,
no. 183(?)
Dumont, Paris   Sale: Paris, February 13, 1854
Cheramy, Paris   Sale: Paris, April 14-16, 1913,
no. 427 or 428
David-Weill, Paris
Acquired from Wildenstein, New York

Publications:
J.–L. Jules David, *Le Peintre Louis David*, Paris,
1880, pp. 656 and 666
A. Dayot, *Un Siècle d'Art, Notes sur la Peinture
Française à l'Exposition Centennale des Beaux-Arts*,
Paris, 1890, p. 38
F. Evrard, "Le Serment du jeu de Paume dans
l'oeuvre de David," *Revue de l'histoire de Versailles
et de Seine-et-Oise*, 1924, pp. 288-289

Exhibitions:
1889 Paris, Exposition Universelle Internationale,
*Catalogue général officiel, Beaux-Arts, Exposition
Centennale de l'Art Français*, no. 1437
1938 New York, Wildenstein, *French XVIIIth
Century Pastels, Watercolors and Drawings from
the David-Weill Collection*, no. 65 or 66
1943 New York, Wildenstein, *The French
Revolution*, no. 40a
1944 New York, Wildenstein, *French Pastels and
Drawings from Clouet to Degas*, no. 103

1947/1948 New York, Wildenstein, *French XIXth
Century Drawings*, no. 8 or 9
1955 Toulouse, Musée des Augustins; Montauban,
Musée Ingres, *Ingres et ses maîtres de Roques à
David*, no. 51
1961 Minneapolis, University Gallery, University
of Minnesota, *The Eighteenth Century: One
Hundred Drawings by One Hundred Artists*,
no. 16
1963 Wildenstein, no. 65 reproduced

The event commemorated in these drawings is the
oath taken by the Third Estate on June 20, 1789, at
Versailles. This group had been denied by Louis
XVI the right to convene in its usual meeting place
(the "Salle des Menus Plaisirs") and so had to
avail itself of the royal tennis court. Here, at the
"jeu de paume," the members took an oath to re-
main assembled until they had established a con-
stitution.

David became officially involved on October
28, 1790, when he was commissioned by the Jacobin
Club to paint the historic event on a canvas of huge
dimensions. At the Salon of 1791 he showed the
drawing which is now in the Louvre. It drew great
attention from the public. Identification of the per-
sonalities depicted was an important element of the
drawing's attraction, despite the fact that the *livret
du Salon* stated that "the artist had no intention of
rendering actual likenesses of the members of the
Assembly."

Most of the many figures in these two draw-
ings are still identifiable (a complete list is given in
V. Lee, "Jacques-Louis David: the Versailles
Sketchbook," *Burlington Magazine*, April 1969).

56 recto: *Bailly standing on desk asking for a vote*

On September 28, 1791, a subscription was voted by the National Assembly in order that the painting be completed at public expense. This device, recommended by Mirabeau, was characteristic of the attitude of the revolutionary leaders toward art and the social and political purposes they attributed to it.

The actual work of the project, however, probably started earlier than the date of the commission. On June 20, 1790, at an anniversary celebration of the Oath, it was proposed that such a painting should be made and David pledged himself to the task. The David sketchbook at Versailles, which is devoted to notes and studies for the Oath, also contains on one of the first pages the inscription: "Ce 14 mars 1790 la veille de mon départ pour Nantes" (V. Lee, op. cit., p. 197). The terms of the October 28 commission gave David four years for the completion of the picture, but in fact he worked on it for only about two years. Many of the figures in the scene had by this time become politically unimportant or undesirable. David himself barely escaped the guillotine. During the Directory, he offered to continue the project with pertinent substitutions for some of the figures, but his offer was not acted upon.

There exists a large amount of work relating to this project. Besides the unfinished painting and several oil sketches of heads, the Musée de Versailles owns a sketchbook, mentioned above, which was one of the three offered in the David sale of 1826. According to Dowd (*Pageant Master of the Republic*, 1948, p. 37, no. 54) the other two were dismembered. The sheets now in the Art Institute were originally part of the album comprising lot no. 71 of the sale. A sheet with four "jeu de paume" sketches on it is also in Versailles (see *Musées de France*, 1913, p. 70).

The drawing now in the Louvre has since its execution been generally regarded as unimpeachable documentation of the event, despite the demonstrable fact that David altered certain facts to accord with the propagandizing purpose of his project (see Brette, *La Révolution Française*, Paris, 1891, p. 385 ff.). Whether or not the artist was actually present at the swearing of the Oath is a problem on which scholars do not agree. The most recent opinion is that of Virginia Lee (op. cit. p. 199) whose conviction that David saw the event in person is based on the hasty and informal style of the verbal notes in the Versailles notebook. Some of the notations in this book do indeed sound as if the writer is reporting actions which he witnessed himself.

The authenticity of our drawings, as well as the similar sheets in the Fogg Art Museum and the three published by Holma, has recently been challenged (cf. Virginia Lee, op. cit. p. 369). To question these drawings would seem tantamount to depriving the history of this great project of its very important first chapter. All these drawings undoubtedly were done when the excitement generated by this awe-inspiring event was still very real, for example the three sketches in Holma's book can only be the work of an eyewitness who also happened to be a great draughtsman capable of capturing the very essence of a dramatic situation in rough sketches. It was only later that David began to work out the various groups and figures, unclothing them and analyzing them in the manner of the High Renaissance. The verso of the second sheet with its figures on a slightly larger scale, particularly the seated figure at the left, can be considered a link to the "analytical" drawings of the Versailles sketchbook. Also, the handwriting in pencil below this drawing appears to be the same as in several pages of that sketchbook.

56 verso: *Large group voting*

Jacques-Louis David

57   *Studies for the Oath of the Tennis Court*
Recto: *Double row of figures*
Verso: *Group with Maupetit de la Mayenne
carried by his two sons*
Brush with grey and black ink over pencil on
ivory paper
290 x 443 mm   1960.558
Collections:
See p. 112

Jacques-Louis David

58 *Profile Portrait of an Old Man (Prieur de la Marne?)*
Black chalk on ivory paper
390 x 230 mm   1960.196

Collections:
Estate of the artist   Sale: Paris, April 17, 1826, included in no. 71 or 72
De Bonadona
Acquired from Jacques Seligmann, New York

Exhibitions:
1963 Wildenstein, no. 66

The identity of the man may well be that of Prieur de la Marne (compare the oil sketch of that same figure at Besançon); however, the dates of execution of the oil sketch and our drawing may be years apart. David Dowd, in a letter, states ". . . the age of the model makes it appear unlikely that it was made as a study for the *Serment du Jeu de Paume,* for Prieur was only 33 at that moment. If one compares the photograph of your drawing with a photograph of David's oil on canvas portrait of Prieur in the Musée de Besançon which was executed in 1791 or 1792 the former appears to be an older Prieur . . . no doubt the sexagenarian with whom David shared his exile in Brussels."

Jacques-Louis David

59   *Sketchbook*
Pencil with occasional use of pen and ink on
ivory paper
Watermark: NAPOLEON EMPEREUR DES FRANÇAIS
ROI D'ITALIE 240 x 190 mm (page size)   1961.393

Collections:
Prince Napoléon (Napoléon Joseph Charles Paul
Bonaparte)
David-Weill, Paris
H. Destailleur
Acquired from Wildenstein, New York

Exhibitions:
1963 Wildenstein, nos. 67-70

In 1804 Napoleon appointed David his Imperial
Court Painter, and commissioned him to com-
memorate in four huge canvases the great ceremonial events of the *Coronation,* the *Distribution
of the Eagles,* the *Reception in the Hôtel de Ville,*
and the *Enthronement in Notre-Dame* (the last
two were never executed). The Art Institute
Sketchbook contains twenty-five preparatory drawings for the *Distribution of the Eagles,* which was
first shown in the Salon of 1810. Twelve portrait
heads are on thinner paper and were mounted onto
the pages of the book. (A full discussion of this
important sketchbook is in preparation.)

60 *Portrait of Jeanbon Saint-André* 1795
Inscribed at bottom center: *L. David*

Inscribed on the mount: *Donum amicitiae. amoris Solatium. David faciebat in vinculis anno R. fr 3 (1795) messidoris 20*

Pen and ink, brown wash, heightened with white on ivory paper
182 mm diameter 1973.153

Collections:
Jeanbon Saint-André, Montauban

Thuet de Caussade (?)

Marquis de Biron Sale: Paris, Georges Petit, 9-11 June 1914, no. 12 reproduced

Oscar Stettiner

Gabriel Cognacq

Publications:
R. Cantinelli, *Jacques-Louis David,* Paris/Brussels, 1930, pl. XLIV

K. Holma, *David, Son Evolution et son Style,* Paris, 1940, p. 120, note 8

D. L. Dowd, *Pageant-Master of the Republic,* Lincoln, Nebraska, 1948, p. 138 and pp. 138-139, note 44

L. Hautecoeur, *Louis David,* Paris, 1954, p. 130

H. Neaf, "Ingres' Frühe Profilbildnisse in Medaillonform," *Pantheon,* XXVIII/3, May-June 1970, p. 224

After the fall of Robespierre on July 26, 1794, many of his followers, including Bonaparte and David, were imprisoned for a short time. It was during his confinement that David made this poignant highly-finished portrait of a fellow-prisoner, Jeanbon Saint-André (1748-1813), who was elected to the Convention in 1792. The bond of friendship that developed quickly between the two men, who were of exactly the same age, is attested by the inscription, which can be read: "A gift of friendship · solace of affection · David made this in confinement in the third year of the French Republic on July 28, 1795."

Later, Saint-André became French Consul in Algiers and Smyrna, and after he had been interned by the Turks for three years, Napoleon named him Conseiller général of the four departments on the left bank of the Rhine. He died in 1813, the year of the First Empire's collapse.

The unusual circumstances which prompted this precious "gift of friendship" resulted in a portrait of great eloquence of characterization.

Donum amicitiæ. amoris Solatium.

David faciebat in vinculis anno R. p. 3 (1795) messidoris 20.

Louis-Philibert Debucourt   Paris 1755 - Belleville 1832

61   *The Dressing Room of the Extras of the Comédie Française*

Inscribed: *Le foyer des figurantes de la Comédie Française*

Grey wash over black chalk on ivory paper
333 x 447 mm   1960.208

Collections:
Maurice Fenaille, Paris
Acquired from Dr. H. Schaeffer, New York
Publications:
Art Quarterly, XXIII, no. 1, Spring 1960,
supplement 5 reproduced

Exhibitions:
1961 Minneapolis, University Gallery, University
of Minnesota, *The Eighteenth Century: One
Hundred Drawings by One Hundred Artists,*
no. 18 reproduced
1963 Wildenstein, no. 72

Debucourt is chiefly known for his superbly skillful color aquatints of contemporary life, which radiate a spirit of bonhomie in the midst of the Revolution. This delightful drawing is reminiscent of his prints, but the dashingly brilliant use of the brush has no parallel in the artist's known drawings, which tend to be meticulous and pedantic. Carle Vernet has also been suggested as an alternative.

La Loge des Figurantes de la Comédie française

62 *Portrait of Jean-Baptiste Belley*
Pencil and estompe heightened with brush in white
354 x 272 mm   1973.156

Collections:
Acquired from Georges Bernier, Paris

Girodet became David's favorite pupil at the age of eighteen. Although David is said to have been disappointed by his later development, Girodet was highly successful in his own day. Contemporary critics saw the grace of Raphael and the power of Michelangelo combined in his *Scene from The Deluge*. Neglected later, interest in his art revived in recent years.

The composition of this sheet is identical with a painting dated 1797 in the Musée de Versailles. It is impossible to say whether this delicately finished drawing is a study for the painting or a souvenir of it. The finesse and precision of execution are astonishing, yet the polished mastery does not interfere in any way with the forceful characterization of what must have been an extraordinary personality with a wise and noble face and sensitive hands.

Jean-Baptiste Belley (1747-1804), a native of Santo Domingo, was elected to the Convention in 1793. In 1802 he was sent to his homeland as Commander-in-Chief to quell the uprisings there, but was returned to France and imprisoned for seditious talk. After his release, he went back to Santo Domingo where he spent his remaining years. He is shown leaning on a marble socle with a bust of G. R. Raynal, philosopher and historian, who had condemned slavery and colonialism even before the Revolution, and whose *History of European Establishments in the Indies* was banned and publicly burned in 1779.

63   *Sheet of studies with the head of La Fornarina and studies of hands for the portrait of Mme de Senonnes*

Inscribed: *Ingres*
Pencil on ivory paper
187 x 208 mm   1972.322

Collections:
Sale: Ingres Atelier (Lugt 1477)
Acquired from William H. Schab, New York

Publications:
The Art Quarterly, xxxv, no. 4, Winter 1972,
p. 439 reproduced p. 449
1971 New York, William H. Schab Gallery,
Master Prints and Drawings, no. 76 reproduced

This delicate and informal study sheet admirably complements the five highly finished portrait drawings by Ingres in The Art Institute. It combines sketches for two celebrated paintings by the master. The inclined head of a young woman is the most memorable feature in *Raphael and La Fornarina,* a theme which so intrigued Ingres that he painted it five times. (What is believed to be the earliest version of 1813 was once in the museum of Riga, but disappeared during the German occupation of 1941; the second, which was shown in the Salon of 1814, is now in the Fogg Art Museum; and the last one was painted as late as 1860). In our drawing the head of the woman is much more inclined than in the Fogg picture, where her posture is almost upright. As the sharply tilted head occurs in all three later versions, it would be reasonable to assume that the drawing was done after the Fogg painting. That the head was done from a live model can be deduced from the very realistic treatment of the folds of the woman's neck.

The three hands in ruffled sleeves are without doubt preliminary studies for one of the artist's noblest female portraits, the Vicomtesse de Senonnes of 1816, in the Musée de Nantes. The very feminine, beautiful hands are one of the glories of that painting, and it is especially the attitude of the sitter's left hand that is rehearsed in our drawing. For Ingres it was easy to express more feminine appeal in a study of hands than most painters can in a full-length portrait.

64 *View of St. Peter's in Rome*
Pencil on ivory paper
337 x 500 mm   1961.31

Collections:
Baron Brincard
Private collection, Switzerland
Acquired from Wildenstein, New York

Publications:
Gazette des Beaux-Arts, LIX, no. 1117 February
1962 supplement, no. 140 reproduced

A. Frankfurter, "'Il bon disegno' from Chicago,"
Art News, LXII, no. 7, November 1963, p. 28
reproduced

This magnificent view of St. Peter's is neither signed nor dated and has therefore been questioned by some scholars, although no one has failed to see the exceptional quality of the drawing. Comparison with some of Ingres' drawings of Rome, especially those of a more sketchy execution, such as plates 72, 74, 75, or figures 13 and 38 in Hans Naef, *Rome vue par Ingres,* Lausanne, 1960, in our opinion, makes the conclusion inevitable that the Art Institute drawing is by the same hand. Even such automatic details as the summary, calligraphic indication of foreground shrubbery is common to all these drawings.

65   *The Tempest*
Watercolor on ivory paper
232 x 210 mm   1965.13

Collections:
P. J. Dedreux-D'Orcy
Vicomte de Fossez
Acquired from Nathan Chaikin

Publications:
L. Eitner, "Géricault's La Tempête,"
Museum Studies, 2, 1967, pp. 6-17 reproduced

Exhibitions:
1971/72 Los Angeles County Museum of Art;
Detroit Institute of Arts; Philadelphia Museum of
Art, *Géricault,* no. 116 reproduced

The very romantic and macabre subject of this
small but extremely powerful watercolor was treated
several times by Gericault (but without the monk)
in the years 1821-23, following his return from
England (see figs. 2-7 in Eitner, op. cit.). It is a
theme very close to the spirit of Byron, whose
poetry was beginning to be widely known in France
at this time.

Eugène Delacroix   Charenton 1798 - Paris 1863

66   *Turkish Officer on Horseback*
Inscribed: *Eug Delacroix*
Gouache and watercolor on ivory paper
252 x 180 mm   1965.455

Collections:
Gustave Revenaz, Paris
Acquired from Wildenstein, New York

Publications:
A. Robaut, *L'oeuvre complète de Eugène Delacroix,* Paris, 1885, no. 565 reproduced

Exhibitions:
1885 Paris, Ecole Nationale des Beaux-Arts, *Exposition Eugène Delacroix,* no. 285

1964 Bern, Kunstmuseum, *E. Delacroix,* no. 169 reproduced

Although Delacroix never visited Turkey, his Moroccan trip in 1832 gave him an insight into the colorful Moslem world. The Turkish rider has no counterpart in the sketches of Arab warriors to be seen in his notebooks. The source of the uniform may be one of the numerous books recording the Greek War of Liberation which ended in 1829. The janissaries were traditionally infantry soldiers but their attire resembled the rider in our drawing, except that their turbans were not red. The rider is perhaps an officer in the Sultan's guard. In this work, the combination of watercolor with gouache enabled Delacroix to obtain more opulent and sparkling color effects than straight watercolor would have made possible.

Eugène Delacroix

67   *Young Lady in the Costume of Manola* 1832
Watercolor on ivory paper
280 x 190 mm   1970.1

Collections:
Estate of the artist   Sale: Paris, Georges Petit,
February 17-29, 1864, no. 578

Eugene Piron

Richy

Acquired from Feilchenfeldt, Zurich

Publications:
A. Robaut, *L'oeuvre complète de Eugène
Delacroix,* Paris, 1885, no. 1648

E. Lambert, "Delacroix et l'Espagne," *Revue des
Arts,* 1951, p. 165

At the end of his Moroccan journey, Delacroix had
an opportunity to visit Spain. He arrived in Cadiz
on the sixteenth of May, 1832, departed for Seville
on the twenty-second, and left Seville on May
twenty-eight. He wrote of his impressions in several
letters to his friend Pierret. In one of these is a
passage which seems particularly applicable to the
Art Institute watercolor. "J'ai vu les belles Es-
pagnoles qui ne sont pas au dessous de leur réputa-
tion. La mantille est ce qu'il y a au monde de plus
gracieux." (Burty, II, p. 182).

Unlike the experience of Morocco, Delacroix's
Spanish visit had no life-long effect on his art. In

fact, after 1832 he did only two paintings of
Spanish themes. Previous to his trip, however,
Delacroix executed a number of such works, generated by his enthusiasm for Goya. In Spain
Delacroix made a large number of drawings from
life (Louvre; Chantilly Collections, Roger-Marx,
H. Lefuel, A. Joubin). Like the Moroccan drawings, they are remarkable in lively observation of
color, movement and detail. Large, single figure
studies are rare among this group. The Roger-Marx
Picador is one of the few examples of a Spanish
subject comparable in size and importance to the
Art Institute drawing.

The notebook (now in the Louvre) that
Delacroix kept during his trip to Spain contains
notations which provide two specific possibilities
for identification of the subject. On May 25 he
refers to having drawn Signora Dolores in half-
figure (Guiffrey, 1909, n. p.). On the following
day he mentions having completed a study of a
mantilla at Mr. Williams', the English consul.

Elie Lambert associates the second of these
notations with a watercolor in the collection of
Maurice Gobin (*Revue des Arts,* 1951, p. 167), of
which he further says the subject "pourrait bien
être une jeune anglaise habituée à vivre en Espagne"
(p. 165). This drawing is a half-length version of
the same model wearing the same costume as that
in the Art Institute watercolor (the *Vente posthume*
catalogue makes this identification, as does Robaut,
no. 1649).

68   *The Three Judges (Les Pièces a Conviction)*
Watercolor over pencil on ivory paper
300 x 465 mm   1968.160

Collections:
Guyotin (?)

Behrens, Hamburg

Baron von Simolin, Berlin

Walter Bareiss, Munich

Acquired from E. V. Thaw, New York

Publications:
E. Fuchs, *Der Maler Daumier*, Munich, 1927,
no. 192a reproduced

K. E. Maison, *Honoré Daumier, Catalogue
Raisonné*, ii, London, 1968, no. 641 reproduced

Exhibitions:
1918 Geneva, Musée d'Art et d'Histoire,
*Tableaux, Dessins et Sculpture de l'Ecole
Française de XIXème Siècle*, no. 154

1955 Bern, Gutekunst & Klipstein, *Auction
Catalogue* 80, no. 5 reproduced

1965 Stuttgart, Staatsgalerie, *Sammlung Walter
Bareiss*

The world of the courtroom, with its unique mixture of pompous grandeur and human frailty and misery, played a great part in Daumier's work ever since he himself had been accused and convicted of a political crime against the tyrannical majesty of Louis-Philippe. While many of these drawings and lithographs are openly satirical, there is an awe-inspiring solemnity in this composition, enhanced by the legs of a large painted Crucifix above the presiding judge in the center. There is an unmistakable nobility and integrity in his countenance which is in remarkable contrast to the boorish peasant face on his left and the shrewdly scrutinizing glance of the colleague on his right. A more complete version of the same composition exists, but some of the subtleties of characterization appear to have been lost in the second version (Maison 642).

Honoré Daumier

69 *Family Scene*
Pen and wash on ivory paper
215 x 205 mm   1965.633

Collections:
Otto Gerstenberg, Berlin
Acquired from Dr. Nathan, Zurich

Publications:
Marées-Gesellschaft, *Daumier,* Munich,
1918 reproduced

E. Fuchs, *Der Maler Daumier,* Munich, 1927,
no. 224a reproduced

H. Leporini, *Die Künstlerzeichnung,* Braunschweig,
1955, no. 100 reproduced

K. E. Maison, *Daumier Drawings,*
New York/London, 1960, no. 56 reproduced

K. E. Maison, *Honoré Daumier, Calalogue
Raisonné,* II, no. 726 reproduced

As a perfect counterpart to another Daumier drawing in the Art Institute collection, *Paternal Discipline,* this is one of the artist's rare idyllic and peaceful family scenes, but there must have been an interval of some fifteen years between the two. The open, quivering pen work, and the illusion of a sunny landscape achieved by a minimum of lines suggest a date around 1865 (cf. the lithographic series, *Croquis de Chasse* and *Croquis d'Automne* of 1864 and 1865.).

Honoré Daumier

70   *The Three Connoisseurs (Les Amateurs de Tableaux)*
Pen and ink with grey and brown wash, heightened with white on ivory paper
Watermark: J WHATMAN/TURKEY MILLS/1869
493 x 392 mm   1968.1

Collections:
Maître Bollet, Lille

Private collection, Paris

Acquired from Wildenstein, New York

Publications:
K. E. Maison, *Honoré Daumier, Catalogue Raisonné*, II, London, 1968, no. 390a reproduced

Considering the general uncertainty of dating the paintings and drawings of Daumier (he himself dated only one painting and neither drawings nor watercolors), it is a lucky incident that the artist made this capital drawing on a sheet of paper bearing a watermark with the date 1869. Several lessons can be drawn from this, the first one being that dating the subject matter is fruitless, because Daumier would often return to certain subjects which he had extensively treated in previous years. The second lesson would be that whenever a painting and a drawing show a nearly identical composition, the drawing should not automatically be assumed to precede the painting.

The late K. E. Maison had sound reasons to date c. 1858/62 a painting which is closely related to our drawing (Maison No. I-133, owned by Mrs. Harris Jonas, New York; in addition there are two oil sketches, I-131 and I-132), but the differences are actually greater than the badly cropped reproduction of our drawing in Maison's catalogue conveys, for it is the marvelous spacious ambience that gives this uncommonly large and brilliant drawing its unmistakable character as a work from the last decade of Daumier's life.

71   *Study for Ugolino*
Inscribed: *J. Bte Carpeaux* 1860
Grey and white gouache, pen and brown ink
on tan paper
622 x 480 mm   1963.264

Collections:
Estate of the artist (Lugt 500)

Mme Clément-Carpeaux   Sale: Paris, Hotel
Drouot, May 31-June 2, 1894, no. 199

Richard S. Davis

Acquired from Jacques Seligmann, New York

Publications:
Museum of Fine Arts, Boston, *Bulletin,* LXII,
no. 330, 1964, p. 140

Exhibitions:
1963 Wildenstein, no. 95 reproduced

As a winner of the Prix de Rome (1858-1862),
Carpeaux was deeply impressed by Michelangelo's
figures for the tomb of Julius II, as well as by
Hellenistic sculpture, such as the Laocoön group,
and he desired to try his hand at a group of similar
dramatic impact. The gruesome ordeal of Ugolino
and his sons from Dante's *Inferno* gave him a
subject suited to his temperament. Faced with the
Academy's restrictions as to subject matter, the
young artist returned to Paris and succeeded in
gaining the support of the Minister of State, Achille
Fould. The model was finished in 1861, acquired
by the state, and cast in bronze. Our drawing,
dated 1860, may well be the finished study that
Carpeaux took to Paris. It shows the artist as a
draughtsman of great power and originality, and
it also proves his admiration for the drawings of
Géricault. Certain expressive, unorthodox exag-
gerations in the anatomy of the main figure were
toned down in the sculpture. This early work at
once established him as the leading sculptor of the
Second Empire. A few years later he made another
version in marble, now in the Metropolitan Museum.

72   *Léon Leenhoff, Standing*
Conté crayon on ivory paper
405 x 205 mm   1963.140

Collections:
J. Mathey
Acquired from Stephan Spector, New York

Publications:
J. Mathey, *Graphisme de Manet,* 1961,
no. 40 reproduced

J. Mathey, "Trois Dessins Inédits de Manet,"
Pantheon, September-October 1966, p. 316 detail
reproduced

Exhibitions:
1963 Wildenstein, no. 97 reproduced

1966-1967 Philadelphia Museum of Art;
Art Institute of Chicago, *Edouard Manet,*
no. 30 reproduced but only shown in Chicago.

In connection with the controversy over some of the works published by J. Mathey (op. cit.), the authenticity of this excellent drawing has been questioned by several scholars (sometimes without knowledge of the original) while it has been accepted by others, including John Rewald. The subject may well be the artist's son, Leon (Koëlla) Leenhoff, who was born in 1852. In that case, the drawing would have to be done in the mid-sixties, which is plausible for stylistic reasons also. A red chalk drawing, also believed to be a portrait of Léon Leenhoff, is in the Museum Boymans-Van Beuningen (cf. *Le Dessin Francais . . . . dans les Collections Hollandaises,* Paris and Amsterdam, 1964, no. 174, pl. 143. The Chicago drawing mentioned on p. 148). The subject of that drawing is certainly a few years older than the boy in the Chicago drawing, and may be of the approximate age of the young man in the Munich painting *Le Petit Dejeuner* of 1868.

147

Edouard Manet

73   *Study of a Seated Nude (La Toilette)*
Red chalk on ivory paper
280 x 200 mm   1967.30

Collections:
Auguste Pellerin Sale: Paris, Hotel Drouot,
May 7, 1926, no. 35 reproduced

Marcel Guérin, Paris

Mme Indig-Guérin

Acquired from Wildenstein, New York

Publications:
R. Rey, *Choix de 64 Dessins de Manet,* Paris, 1932,
pl. 10

G. Jedlicka, *Edouard Manet,* Zurich, 1941,
p. 251 reproduced

B. Degenhart, *Europäische Handzeichnungen,*
Berlin/Zurich, 1943, no. 164

J. Mathey, *Graphisme de Manet,* 1961,
pp. 14-15 reproduced

A. de Leiris, *The Drawings of Edouard Manet,*
Berkeley/Los Angeles, 1969, no. 186 reproduced

Exhibitions:
1932 London, Royal Academy of Arts,
*Commemorative Catalogue of the Exhibition of
French Art* 1200-1900, no. 874, reproduced

1932 Paris, Musée de l'Orangerie, *Exposition
Manet,* no. 106

1937 Paris, Palais National des Arts,
Chefs d'Oeuvre de l'Art Français, no. 686

The drawings of Manet have needed a much longer time to find favor with collectors than his paintings and watercolors. The reason is that they are often diametrically opposed to the academic concept of what a drawing is or should be. If Rembrandt exasperated some of his contemporary critics by his lack of concern for the "correct" classical method, the sins of Manet provoked even greated ire. To be sure, Manet was not the practiced, untiring draughtsman Degas was: when he drew he did so entirely from the painter's point of view. No better example could be found than this sanguine drawing of a nude, *La Toilette.* It is a miraculous study of light playing on the soft texture of a female body, done with total disregard for anatomical correctness or the then prevailing concepts of beauty of form. In this respect, the drawing may well be compared with the nude studies of Rembrandt from the late 1650s. Although we have every reason to assume that the artist had a painting in mind, it did not materialize, and the work closest to our drawing is the etching *La Toilette,* published in 1862. A preliminary drawing for the etching is owned by the Courtauld Institute.

149

Edouard Manet

74   *Portrait of Berthe Morisot*
Watercolor on ivory paper
205 x 165 mm   1963.812

Collections:
Durieux-Cassirer, Berlin
M. Oppenheim, Berlin
Acquired from J. K. Thannhauser

Publications:
Marées Gesellschaft, *Edouard Manet,*
Munich, 1922, pl. 10
P. Jamot, "Manet," *Les Beaux-Arts,* 1932, 1,
no. 238 p. 148
A. Tabarant, *Manet et ses Oeuvres,* Paris,
1947, p. 258
A. de Leiris, *The Drawings of Edouard Manet,*
Berkeley/Los Angeles, 1969, no. 434 reproduced

Exhibitions:
1966-1967 Philadelphia Museum of Art;
Art Institute of Chicago, *Edouard Manet,*
no. 110 reproduced

Manet was introduced to Berthe Morisot in 1868 by the painter Henri Fantin-Latour, and during the next five years, her dark-eyed, sensitive and animated face appeared in ten paintings, two lithographs, and one etching. She possessed the kind of beauty that evoked memories of Spain in Manet, and he made her the principal figure in *The Balcony* of 1868, his magnificent tribute to Goya. When he painted her for the last time in the autumn 1874, shortly before her marriage to his younger brother Eugène, he again added a Spanish touch with shawl and fan. The shawl is black because her father had died in January.

The painting, owned by the Rouart family, has a somber undertone, perhaps a hint of resignation, but the watercolor of the same composition is completely enchanting in its animation. The technique of watercolor was best suited for this kind of transitory attitude which suggests lively conversation. Although some of Manet's watercolors are souvenirs of his paintings rather than studies for them, in this case everything speaks for the precedence of the watercolor.

75   *At the Door*
Blue crayon and black wash heightened with white
on buff paper
470 x 235 mm   1965.22

Collections:
Colonel Wild

Mutiaux

Scharf

Acquired from Dr. Nathan, Zurich

Publications:
M. G. Dortu, *Toulouse-Lautrec et son oeuvre,*
New York, 1971, v, no. D.2.899 reproduced

In 1884 or 1885, Toulouse-Lautrec moved to Montmartre. At first he lived with his friends René and Lily Grenier in a house opposite Degas' studio. In 1885, Aristide Bruant opened his cabaret, Le Mirliton, where Lautrec and the Greniers became steady customers. Bruant, a gifted singer and poet, created a new style of realistic ballads about the lives of people in the poorest sections of Paris. He also had a habit of insulting his audiences with biting personal remarks, which delighted them. For Lautrec, the southern aristocrat, Bruant opened a new world of social concern, and this is reflected particularly in those works for which a poor young laundress, Carmen Gaudin, served as a model. Our drawing, showing a shy young woman in a hesitant gesture at a half-open door, belongs to this group, which also includes the paintings *A Montrouge* of 1888 and *La Blanchisseuse* of 1889. François Gauzi, another friend of Lautrec's made a photograph of Carmen Gaudi standing in a half-open door, and this may have inspired Lautrec's drawing. Bruant asked Lautrec to illustrate some of his songs, and Lautrec complied with four contributions, some of which are signed "Treclau", to spare his family the embarrassment of having an artist in the clan.

The composition of this drawing anticipates devices used by Bonnard, Vuillard, and others of the Nabis group a few years later. Perhaps the last echo of it is a drawing of Bonnard of 1941, *Woman at an Open Door (Bonnard and His Environment,* Museum of Modern Art, N.Y., 1964, p. 24), but instead of the slanting bottom edge of Lautrec's drawing, which is not an accident but a compositional necessity, Bonnard placed a laundry basket in the lower left corner.

76   *The King's Card Game (Le Besigue du Roi)*
      Watercolor and black chalk on ivory paper
      291 x 228 mm   1969.271

Collections:
Mourgues
Romain Coolus
Private collection, Paris
Acquired from Wildenstein, New York

Publications:
M. G. Dortu, *Toulouse-Lautrec et son Oeuvre*, III,
New York, 1971, no. A.223 reproduced

Lautrec made four illustrations in watercolors for Romain Coolus' novel, "La Belle et la Bête," which were reproduced in *Le Figaro illustré,* no. 66, September 1895. Perhaps it was the success of this composition that induced him to repeat it as a monochrome lithograph (Delteil 115), of which one example was hand-colored.

77   *Mlle Cocyte*
Signed: *T. Lautrec*
Pencil, red chalk, heightened with white
350 x 255 mm
The Joseph and Helen Regenstein Collection
1965.14

Collections:
Heim (sale, Paris, 30 April 1913, no. 12, as
Au Cafe Concert)
Eugène Blot (sale, Paris, 2 June 1933, no. 22)
M. Bergaud, Paris
Duhem

Publications:
M. Joyant, *T.-L., Paris*, 1927, p. 241
reproduced p. 143
G. Jedlicka, *T.-L.,* Berlin, 1929 reproduced p. 133
Gerstle Mack, *T.-L.,* New York, 1942, p. 214
Pierre Lavalée, *Le dessin français,* Paris, 1948,
p. lix
M. G. Dortu, *T.-L.,* Paris, 1952, p. 10, fig. 58
C. G. Heise, *Grosse Zeichner des xix jahrhunderts,*
Berlin, 1959
M. G. Dortu, *T.-L. et son Oeuvre,* New York,
1971, vol. vi, p. 902, no. D.4 642

Toulouse-Lautrec spent the last winter of his tragically short life in Bordeaux. His family and friends hoped that removed from the many distractions of Paris, he would recuperate from the ravages of his dissipated mode of living (which miraculously failed to reduce his capacity for work) in a quiet provincial atmosphere offering some amenities of city life. One of the glories of Bordeaux has always been its Opera House, and Toulouse-Lautrec became a regular visitor. The performance which seems to have pleased him most and which he mentioned in several letters was Offenbach's *La Belle Hélène.* The unabashed vulgarity and vitality of the singer of the title role, Mlle Cocyte, fascinated him, and he made several sketches of her, but none is more charming and vivacious than this drawing, executed with so few but meaningful and expressive lines. If any single drawing could be said to convey the essence of Lautrec's mastery in his last years, this sheet would qualify admirably.

James Ensor   Ostende 1860 - 1949

78   *Portrait of the Artist's Niece in Chinese Costume*
Inscribed: recto, *J. Ensor 99.* Verso, *Portrait de ma
nièce Madame R. Daveluy, fille de Madame Marie
Ensor, peint en 1899./J. Ensor*
Watercolor over pencil, retouched in pen and ink
638 x 497 mm   1972.426

Collections:
Camille Gutt, Brussels   Sale: London, Sotheby
& Co., 12 April 1972, no. 87 reproduced
Acquired from E. V. Thaw, New York

Publications:
Grégoire Le Roy, *James Ensor,* Brussels & Paris,
1922, p. 187

This enchanting, unusual, and important work by
Ensor has apparently escaped notice by the artist's
biographers, beyond the mere listing of a watercolor
"La petite chinoise" of 1899 by Le Roy in 1922.
The charming little girl, completely in control of
the Oriental demons surrounding her, is the artist's
niece, Alexandra (later Mme Daveluy), daughter
of the artist's sister Marie, from her unhappy and
short-lived marriage to a Chinese. The Art Institute
also owns a charcoal drawing of Marie by the artist,
dated 1881.

Berthe Morisot

Georges Seurat   Paris 1859 - 1891

81 *Landscape with Trees*
Conté crayon on ivory paper
620 x 470 mm   1966.184

Collections:
Family of the artist

Mme Leopold Appert

Private collection, Paris

Acquired from Wildenstein, New York

Publications:
H. Dorra and J. Rewald, *Seurat: l'oeuvre peint: biographie et catalogue critique,* Paris, 1959, no. 116a reproduced

C. M. de Hauke, *Seurat et son oeuvre,* Paris, 1961, no. 619 reproduced

Exhibitions:
1957 Paris, Musée Jacquemart-Andre, *Seurat,* no. 29

1958 Art Institute of Chicago and New York, Museum of Modern Art, *Seurat Paintings and Drawings,* no. 71

Numerous figure studies for Seurat's masterpiece, *La Grande Jatte* (1884-1886) in The Art Institute, are known but only a few are concerned with the terrain itself. The sinuous, gracefully curved and almost humanized tree trunk in the foreground and the sharply bent tree in the middle ground are motifs which appear to have been combined into a single tree in the painting, but the individual character of the tree trunk has been abandoned. The low-keyed range of tonalities suggests a gentle mist rising from the water, and the elusive luminosity produces an aura of silent communication with nature, which is foreign to the painting itself and recalls the mood of the Symbolist painters.

Edouard Vuillard   Cuiseaux, Soane-et-Loire 1868 - La Baule 1940

82   *Evening in the Garden of the Alcazar*
      Inscribed: *E. Vuillard*
      Distemper on cardboard
      482 x 425 mm   1964.2

Collections:
Georges Bernheim

Felix Fenéon   Sale: Paris, Hotel Drouot, 30 May
1947, no. 58 reproduced

(Bought by Theodore Schempp and sold to
Jacques Seligmann)

Roger Dametal

Acquired from J. K. Thannhauser

The nocturnal subject with its mysterious light
effect, as well as the technique of oil on untreated
cardboard (see the essay on Vuillard's technique by
Jacques Salomon in John Russell, *Vuillard,* New
York, 1971, pp. 137 ff.) point to a date in the early
or middle 1890's, rather than 1924, as suggested in
the Fenéon Sale Catalogue.